THE MUSIC OF THE SOUL LIVES ON ON ON ON

A Henry Mackaman Experience

Created by Hanna Kjeldbjerg

D1219736

Written by Henry Mackaman
Created by Hanna Kjeldbjerg
Proofread by Alicia Ester and Taylor Blumer

ISBN 13: 978-1-59298-762-7
Library of Congress Catalog Number: 2017951301
Printed in the United States of America
First Printing: 2018
22 21 20 19 18   6 5 4 3 2

Design concept by Shannon Fletcher
Cover artwork and flip-book illustrations by Margaret Palmquist

BEAVER'S POND
PRESS

7108 Ohms Lane
Edina, MN 55439–2129
(952) 829-8818
www.BeaversPondPress.com

For more information, visit www.HenryMackaman.com.

THE MUSIC OF THE SOUL LIVES ON ON ON ON ON

A Henry Mackaman Experience

Created by Hanna Kjeldbjerg

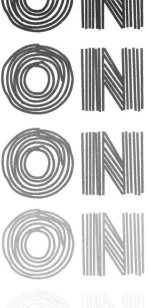

PRAISE FOR
THE MUSIC OF THE
SOUL LIVES ON

"The book captures a child and later a young man who was witty, intelligent, charming and who loved and was loved by many. I am so impressed. This book holds a special place in my Office at the Capitol."
—Lori Swanson, Minnesota Attorney General

"Henry's subjects reflect his age and experience, are essentially positive and sunny, but reflect someone grappling with the emptiness that sometimes looms behind our lives together. Henry's death feels more unfair after having read his book because his work feels cut short. Henry's love for the people in his life comes through in his stories. His writing was a labor of love: for music, for travel and new experiences, for youth, for adventure, and for you."
—Ryan Winkler, former Minnesota state representative for District 46A

""Henry seems to have the ability to move from poetry to music to prose flawlessly, all the while being able to develop deep, lasting friendships with just about anyone he met. This book gives the sense of a person dancing just above the earth."
—Milt Snoeyenbos, professor of philosophy Georgia State University (retired)

"I am so moved by Henry's life and those that were touched by his spirit. I am equally impressed by how this book draws this all into one breath. So much was lost to the world with Henry's death, but truly the music of his soul lives on, which is now music to my soul . . . and so many others."
—Benjamin Allen, author of *Out of the Ashes: Healing in the Afterloss*

"The craftsmanship of The Music of the Soul Lives On is superb—weaving Henry's art, history, humor and life's views with the writings of friends, family, and writing students makes for a unique and meaningful book, and a thoroughly enjoyable read. I'm glad to know Henry Mackaman today."
—Mike Tikkanen, creator of KARA, author of *Invisible Children*

"Henry's book is remarkable, beautifully eclectic and well done. It is unique, unlike any other volume on the shelf."
—Dr. David Ness, family physician.

"This book is spiritual, I feel like I am holding Henry in my hand, at least a part of what was deep in his soul."
—Mary Paulsen

"This book is absolutely awesome. Every attention to detail has been worked into the book and it is such a great tribute to a fascinating young man."
—Dave Black, general manager for WSUM

"

You're listening to
WSUM, 91.7 FM
Madison, tuning in to
The Grooving Tree.

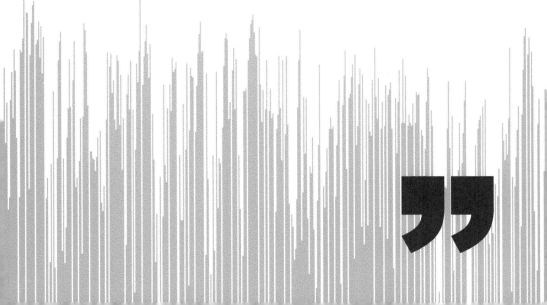

This is Henry.

"

NOVEMBER 10
1991
–
APRIL 10
2013

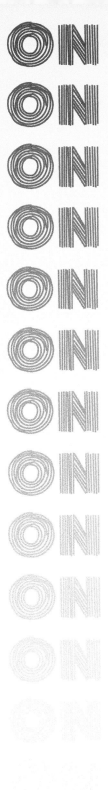

Thank-you mom, for
all   you've done for me.
You taught the spirit of giving.
    My wallet is empty,
but my heart is full,

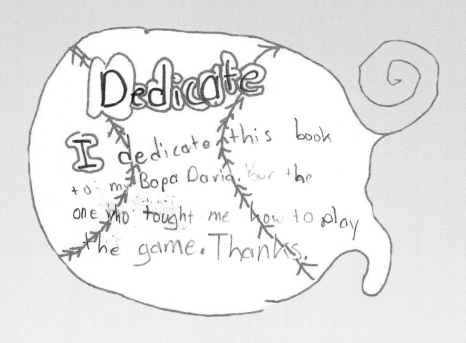

Dedicate

I dedicate this book to my Bopa David. Your the one who tought me how to play the game. Thanks.

Dedicated to my Grandma Cordy, you make my life a little bit sweeter.

CONTENTS

FOREWORD

By David Strand, Henry's Grandpa

The book you are holding contains the creative writing of Henry Douglas Mackaman. Born in Oakland, California in November 1991, Henry's physical life ended in April 2013 at Meriter Hospital in Madison, Wisconsin.

The son of Meredith, a pharmacist, and Douglas, who had a newly minted history PhD from the University of California, Berkeley, the family first settled in Hattiesburg, Mississippi, where Dad taught at the University of Southern Mississippi.

Henry's first school was Sacred Heart Catholic School in Hattiesburg. The school administrators included three nuns who were next-door neighbors. They invited non-Catholic Henry to attend, and soon he earned the nickname among faculty and friends as "Saint Henry." Henry loved the school, where he was selected by the Holy Father to carry the Host during First Communion celebrations.

Henry was a storyteller, beginning as a child. He was instinctively captivated by stories told around a beach fire at his beloved Cedar Lake. His contributions to serial stories—started and then handed off to the next person—were always the most intricate, evocative, and scary. (They often frightened his little brother, Owen.) He recorded his stories and experiences in the journals that he loved to keep. Many turned into mini-books such as *Henry & Grandma's Magic Pancakes* and *Trips to the Twins*, the former of which you can find in this book. We didn't know it then, but these small hand-made books were just the beginning of Henry's determination to create and document.

Henry and his family moved to Saint Paul, where he attended Webster Elementary, Ramsey Middle School, and finally Saint Paul Central High School. He played the saxophone well enough to join the Central High Symphony and Pep Band. He played baseball, mastered skateboarding, won a junior tennis tournament and a free throw shooting contest (against adult contestants) at Grand Old Day, and developed guitar skills abetted by his naturally double-jointed fingers.

Henry's writings and handmade things are his legacy. Included in this book are drawings, joke books, Christmas cards, skateboards, a guitar called "the Shig," several movies, his music (including CD album covers), and his collaboration with high school friend Simon Alexander to produce the illustrated storybook, *Just Birds* (which was a part of a civics class assignment on diversity and became a finalist in the B'nai B'rith International Diverse Minds Youth Writing Challenge).

Upon high school graduation, Henry chose the University of Wisconsin-Madison, where both parents had earned degrees in the eighties. Henry tested out of entry level courses for his double major of Economics and Creative Writing, meaning he already was taking sophomore-level UW-Madison courses by his first semester.

In a way, Henry made love to life, and he discovered much to love at Madison, quickly finding outlets for his creative interests. He tended bar at the Student Union, worked shifts at Murfie, a local music store, and hosted a weekly disc jockey show on the WSUM campus radio station, and all before the end of his first two months at Madison.

Vital, even celebrated, in Henry's short life was his personal adage, the "courage to continue." Whatever attracted his curiosity became his pursuit to master. I hope that Henry's example can be an inspiration to others, as it has become for me. After showing him how to bait a fishhook just once, he later wrote, "What kind of fisherman can't bait his own hook?" He was only four years old.

I soon learned to admire that urgent persistence as I witnessed his relentless, often painful, mastery of skateboard acrobatics. He literally never gave up, and had the scrapes and bruises as proof of merit. Write a short story? Produce and make a movie? Build a guitar? Start his own band? Become a radio disc jockey? Give comfort to a troubled friend? It all came to pass, absent of insecure hesitation in the beginning or a triumphant end zone spike at the close. That wasn't Henry.

We remember Henry. Each year a group retraces his last steps to the hospital ER after he awoke deathly sick at 3:00 a.m. on Monday, April 8, 2013. Each May we attend the UW-Madison English Department's awarding of the Henry Douglas Mackaman Undergraduate Writer's Award, their highest award for an undergrad writing student. We visit the location of park benches inscribed in his honor, one overlooking the Mississippi River two miles from his Saint Paul home, and another at the Henry Villas Zoo in Madison. Appropriately, it is located facing the African lion exhibit and states: "For Henry, who had the heart of a lion." Henry's mom has embarked on a cause to educate college-age students about the warning signs of bacterial meningitis, the disease that took Henry's life, and has distributed thousands of refrigerator magnets drawing attention to its symptoms around the nation.

Henry's raw creative writing ability and style are revealed in the stories and poetry included in this anthology. For his youthful twenty-one years, he displayed an uncommon range of genres in his short stories. Clearly mysterious end-of-life drama was a frequent theme (Every Man Needs a Companion). He also wrote slapstick adventure comedy (The Misadventures of Burchard and Hawkins), fantasy (Tom Copper's Wax Graveyard), and quirky family dynamics (Lucidity, Come Back to Me).

Another side of Henry is revealed in his descriptive notes about exploring new places and meeting new people on his travels. You will discover this in "Journals: Henry in Europe." This is particularly interesting to me because having visited most of the same places, I can't help admiring the way his descriptions evoke a resonant animation about the scenes he reveals.

If Henry seemed impatient and in a hurry, it may have been because he sensed he had so little life to spare. Did he somehow know he had a doomsday clock ticking away? His life was cut short so suddenly, and it is deeply unfair that the world didn't get to know him beyond age twenty-one. But in fact, Henry lives on. People who never were lucky enough to know him can find out who he was by reading his writing and listening to his music.

The story of the Titanic, one that he discovered at age six, became his metaphor. Both had physical lives cut short by tragic events. Henry's fateful iceberg was the lethal disease bacterial meningitis. The Titanic sank on April 15, 1912. Henry's life ended just five days short of that very day, 101 years later. Like the captain of the great ship, Henry did not see it coming. Lifeboats saved hundreds from the sinking Titanic. Henry's lifeboats are his vital organs, organs that he pledged by becoming a donor, that were given to five people in order that they may live. The music theme of the 1997 Titanic movie is "My Heart Will Go On." Henry's heart is still beating, and goes on in the chest of Professor Walter Goodman.

One month after his death, Henry was post-humously awarded a BA degree in Economics and Creative Writing. UW-Madison waived the one credit he was short, even though he was just completing his third year of study.

Finally, I have testimonials from two people who knew Henry: one from his writing teacher, and a second from one of his closest friends.

Alyssa Knickerbocker was a professor at UW-Madison and taught Henry in a creative writing class. She said:

> Henry's writing had an unforgettable blend of insight and humor. What I remember about his stories is that they were irreverent, but with an emotional core. He had the rare ability to be funny and meaningful at the same time, to write fiction that had both levity and weight.
>
> Music played a huge role in almost all of his writing—his stories always seemed to have a soundtrack playing through them, driving the plot, teasing emotions out of his characters, or out of you, the reader. He wasn't afraid to try out wild or

absurd plot twists, just to see where they would take him—sometimes, writers forget how valuable that kind of fearless exploration can be!

When I think of Henry, and his writing, I think of his sweet, sly sense of humor, and how vividly that always came across in his work.

Ola Lisowski is one of Henry's closest friends from UW-Madison. She wrote this on the first anniversary of his death:

> On this day one year ago I said good-bye to one of the greatest friends I'll ever have. He was warm and he was gentle—he was welcoming and always thoughtful. He made me feel more a part of anything than I ever felt before. He was sincere. He mattered. He matters. He will always matter to those of us who love him and will forever miss the smile that curled around his teeth and that gait so unique to him.
>
> He found the house we live in, toured it, and was the first signature on the lease. He was the center of so many things, including most of our friendships. He brought so many people together, in life and in death. He shared my passion for travel, discovery of cultures, asking why. And grooving the whole way there and back. I got to watch him fall in love, something I'll always cherish.
>
> Sometimes I miss him so much, and he seems so far away, but I only need to listen to one of the dozens of bands he introduced me to and I can see myself back in the old apartment, laptops side-by-side with him, exchanging thoughts on music and culture and politics and our families and everything that came to mind, because he was the kind of guy to whom you could talk about literally anything. He carried an open mind, a patient mind, a warm and loving mind.
>
> The loss of one incredible person has changed the lives of so many—because so many loved him. And we will always carry him with us. I am confi-

dent that he made me a better person.

Today is for him, but really, every day is for him, I won't ever forget him and the way he changed me and so many others. I love him and always will. His name was Henry Mackaman and he was only twenty-one. Wherever you are, Henry, you're always on our minds.

So, dear reader, turn the pages and get to know Henry Mackaman, a gentle and courageous soul with a heart big enough to accommodate friends, both past and future. I was luckier than most who knew him. He was my grandson and companion, and now he is my own North Star reminding me every day: What would Henry do?

David Strand
Cedar Lake, 2017

Normandy 2012
Watercolor by Duane Barnhart.

A LETTER TO HENRY

from his Grandma, Cordy Strand

Dear Henry,

I think of you every day and miss you all of the time. My heart aches. But you know that, don't you? I tell you often enough.

Sometimes you come by in my dreams and those are the best nights. When I wake in the morning, my being feels comforted, filled with love and warmth. It makes me wonder just "where are you?" You seemed so real last night.

I keep a memory box now. There are pictures of you from the day you were born until the day you left. There are the drawings that you and Owen made for me (and of me!). The one of "Gramma working as a clown juggling two basketballs on a skateboard" still makes me giggle. There are the birthday cards and Valentines you designed, the little books you wrote, the poems you composed and later turned into songs for me. I have a picture of you sitting on my kitchen stool strumming and singing, "Gramma when you are old and cannot make the stair, don't you worry, Gramma, I will buy you a roller chair."

Then there are the notes and letters, later the e-mails that I treasure. One is particularly endearing. You wrote that you were proud of me and proud to be my grandson and hoped that "one day I too can harness the power of my passions and do something great."

In the box is the small Twins uniform you asked me to sew for you "and Gramma, make it with the stripes going down." There is your worn and ragged blue flannel shirt that I wear when nothing else can warm me, the socks you wore the last night when you walked yourself back to the hospital, the little Buddha you brought me from London, and a stone that you told me would bring me strength from the earth.

Lastly in the box is a small container of your ashes, a lock of your soft brown hair, and a plaster cast of your right hand.

Memories, beautiful memories of a beautiful boy that I was blessed to have as a grandson. These memories of you will always light the darkest days with the peace and radiance that was you.

Love forever,
Gramma C

A Note:

The font used in this book was created by Margaret Palmquist, using the lettering found in Henry's journals and written in his own hand.

The color palette was chosen to reflect Henry's love of water . . . the varying blues of our lakes and rivers, and the deep blue of the sea. Yellow represents the sunshine and brightness of his life . . . a radiance that he so generously shared with those of us who knew and loved him.

A LETTER TO THE READERS

from Henry's Mom, Meredith

Henry was born into a world that desperately needed him.

He was a gift to me and his organ recipients, and this book is his gift to you.

Although his life on this earth was far too short, it is apparent that he knew his days were numbered. So he lived his life accordingly.

He gave us so much joy with his goofy smile and his witty remarks, and all the while he was busy creating. Creating songs, stories, and happy memories that we will never forget. We all knew just how much he loved us.

I am so proud and amazed at all of his accomplishments—athletic, musical, and academic. And now, after his death, I can see how he inspired countless people. He truly does live on in all of us.

Henry once said, "You have to try and love this world, even though it might not love you back."

Oh sweet Henry, how right you were!

I miss him more with each passing day.

Meredith Leigh

BACK CAMPUS: ABOUT THE COVER ART

By Margaret Palmquist

I should have listened to my mom.

When I couldn't function, didn't want to move, didn't want to eat, didn't know how to distract myself, my mom told me to try writing down my memories of Henry.

But I couldn't.

I could vomit words onto a page about my grief, about my love for him, about trying to grasp the unknown. Wax poetic on what I hoped death was like and the ways in which I felt lost. That, I remember.

I should have listened to my mom, though, because I want to express some of Henry's feelings now, and to do that, I must open the vault of my memories of him. The problem is they're convoluted. I can conjure up the more important ones, the ones I comfort myself with, but so many other memories feel like a dream upon waking. Bleary-eyed, I try to study certain aspects of the less significant or romantic or overtly funny times—if I had just written something down as soon as I woke up!—but, like dreams, only a few things become clear while the rest . . . it makes me want to just go back to sleep. Because maybe if I sleep more, it'll help me recall.

Or maybe I'm just hoping I'll dream about him again and it'll actually be him instead of just a cheap subconscious stand-in
> but maybe not,
> as then I'll wake up and be disappointed and realize sometimes I prefer the stand-in because I don't cry when I visit only with dream prop Henry
>> and I always cry when he seems real and I awake only to force myself to remember
>> he's gone
>> and I always cry when I realize that my fuzzy memories
>>> are intangible,
>>> are wouldn't-hold-up-in-court evidence,
>>> are all I have left to prove he was ever here.

I've tried to conjure a memory of Henry's through one of my own. I don't remember when it was. Sometime before he died, obviously. His memory, however, I know was from mid-September 2012.

I don't know what it is about a certain personality type, but Henry and I were both rolled with the stay-up-until-4 a.m., get-up-at-1 p.m. lifestyle. Not that we were lazy (well, he wasn't lazy); night was when our brains worked.

One such night—was it March? or February? definitely still winter—I had already gone to sleep but he hadn't—or had I just gotten off a shift at 2 a.m.? —anyway, we were in his room and it was late. Dark. No, definitely late.

Henry wanted to talk before we went to sleep. He had been working on a song, his last not-quite-finished song, called "Back Campus." The pieces were there but as he played with his free trial of Pro Tools, I remember the frustrated look on his face because it was slowing down his computer and he couldn't close it or he'd lose his progress. And he couldn't save it because he'd have to buy the software. And he was twenty-one and couldn't shell out $600. That, I remember. Stupid numbers. Henry's annoyed expression.

He wanted to talk then. Was it before or after he found out he was going to have another little sibling? On that night, he was happy. In this memory, he was feeling lost.

I can only attempt (and I won't) to invent the words we said. But I do recall the ideas behind them.

Why wasn't he able to capture the feeling of Back Campus?

First, he had me listen to the song.

While he had told me before about his trip to perform at Earlham College in September 2012, he wanted to see if I could grasp the sentiment he was trying to convey about an experience there.

He and his bandmates and another friend were exploring the area one afternoon. They were walking around in a somewhat secluded, somewhat just ig-nored part of the school called, you know, Back Cam-pus. He said there were a lot of trees—a forest? or just trees?—and either the remnants of a forgotten con-struction process or one just put on hold. There was a dirt pit and there were large concrete cylinders jutting out over the pit. That, I remember. His friends were goofing around nearby but he didn't feel silly or very sociable.

He walked out onto a cylinder and as he drifted away from the others physically, he drifted away alto-gether and—was it dusk? or still light? —stared out at the trees and felt that incorporeal feeling and listened to how small his world was. He stood there for an eternity. Maybe he's still there.

As I listened to him describe it, I felt as though I had entered his memory in a way I never quite have before or since. I stood there and experienced it with him. We had never felt smaller but we never felt small. And what he wanted to communicate was the incom-municable, but he somehow allowed me to join him in the confusion.

Back Campus made him want to share things because that was all that felt important in that moment, standing in the sky. He went from inconsequential to the only person in the world to not existing himself. In solitude, he felt the need to make other people understand that feeling of making people want to understand. In solitude, he felt most connected.

He had me listen to the song again. Suddenly, neither of us was in the room.

How could I communicate that message?

I tried to draw Back Campus many times, before he died, so I could share it with him. But it proved nearly as hard as making the track sound exactly right.

I kept trying after he died. I couldn't make it work. I'd forget about it for weeks. I couldn't even write down the memory of him telling me his memory and it began to become muddled. But in my attempts to capture it, some things stuck. The longer I would let myself stop everything and think about Henry, the more I was able to conjure that night. Never the words, just the ideas.

I hope, in the cover, you feel something like what he wanted. That maybe I helped you understand. I hope in some line of the illustration, you find yourself wanting to share your own solitude with someone, that you and them and we might all be alone together.

Like what you'll find in his writing.

Like what he made people feel.

Like what he wanted.

That, I remember.

The font used for quotes throughout this book I have decided to call "Henry Mackahand." The series of images at the page bottoms is similarly titled "Flippy Bookaman."

It was his dying wish to live on in this way. Obviously.

I've had so much time. Like everyone else, I scold myself for using it irresponsibly. Once I have infinity at my fingertips, surely then I will do all those things I meant to.

When I had a lot of time, I pored over old homework sheets and notebook pages of Henry's. I practiced his handwriting until it made sense to me. Because the Internet is amazing, I knew already that there was a free service with which one could convert handwriting into fonts. I have a font saved of my own handwriting, of course, which I think is mainly what people create.

But I like thinking of the custom writing website as a service for the bereaved. Imagine! Typing a letter to yourself in your loved one's hand, making believe it is all they meant to say. Imagine! Writing out thoughts as though they're talking through you. Imagine! Leaving notes for yourself from your dead friend, pretending he just popped out to the grocery store.

- Bread   - Eggs
- Spinach   - I love you

I kept Henry Mackahand as my default font for a while. For every time I had something to say; late at night, my inane ramblings would become his; documenting my days, the office would become Henry describing my life in vivid detail; trying out beginnings to stories, I would feel not so very far from his imagination.

When I had a lot of time, I made the flip-book for this Henry Mackaman experience. I knew I wanted to do that before I thought of doing the font. Henry remained a consistent soul but an evolving person throughout his life. Except maybe I just wanted to draw cats and records and birds in his honor.

Have fun moving through it!

Or don't think about it too much.

Or just think about it whenever you have time.

"

If you've been listening, you're aware that I'm alone in the studio tonight. I am alone. There is no one else here. No Andrew Hinkens, no Alec Schacherl, it's just Henry Mack on The Grooving Tree tonight.

And you know what, I find it almost a little bit awkward to be here by myself. I feel like I'm just talking to myself, whereas when I'm with Andrew and Alex I feel like I'm engaging in conversation. I feel like I'm just talking into a microphone.

And the irony is, in fact, I am
just talking into a microphone, but
hopefully, hopefully people are listening
on the other end. It's like on a
playground, you know, talking through
tin cans.

But, you know,
I hope you're listening.

Early on we knew Henry was someone very special. When he was just three years old, Doug, Meredith, Cordy, and I visited the French Quarter in New Orleans for a day. Before lunch we noticed people taking horse-drawn carriage rides.

The service was slow and Henry fussed a little, so we engaged him in talk about the upcoming ride. One of us asked Henry what name he would like the horse to have (they were mostly mules).

Henry thought and said, 'I would like her to be named Rosie.'

After lunch, we headed to the first carriage in line at the curb and climbed in. You could have knocked us over with a feather when the driver turned and said,

'Rosie knows this town well and will show you around New Orleans.'

David "Bapa" Strand
Henry's grandpa

BOOKENDS

"What now?"

Somehow the phrase slips all the way up from my dusty windpipe into the lonely realm of audible self-commentary. Soggy, pruned, and bored, I float with no company other than the sun and the occasional wave, each new arrogant crest as indifferent to my peculiar plight as the last. The sun is no friend of mine either. I am convinced that he wishes to hard-boil my salted body, perhaps for the purpose of creating a brave new side dish for a cosmic brunch.

"Mars, try some of the hard-boiled organic matter," he will say. "I do believe it's *sun* of my best work." While I am pondering the social tendencies of a large ball of burning hydrogen, a faint rumbling tickles my ear.

The wheezing ship isn't far away, coughing quick clouds of smoke as it approaches. Altering my frail body from the dead man's float, I begin to slowly rock my arms back and forth to signal for assistance. The gold coin in my right hand sticks firmly to my skin like a metallic wart. (Why is it there? Can anybody see me? What if the ship thinks I'm an adventurous, unanchored buoy perhaps spinning in circles to avoid confusion?)

Feeling validated by the ship's continued progress, I begin to spin a bit faster. Spinning is hard work, though, and the ship hasn't signaled any notice of my effort. Moving out of the way is not an option; I've invested the last of my energy into the dizzying distress signal. As its thick shadow descends upon my unmoving body the thought suddenly occurs to me that perhaps buoys *do* spin.

The imposing vessel is as large as four elephants stacked on top of two other elephants, and is only five elephants away when a net descends from the deck. Perhaps a vacationing casting director caught sight of my riveting buoy performance and wants my contact information for a callback. I've always known acting is my calling; I starred in my seventh grade class production of Schulz's *Peanuts* as Linus Number Two. The net scoops me up in one swoop—I wonder what my signing bonus will be? The rising net is not as comforting as Linus' iconic blue blanket, but I am glad to escape the sun's ingredient list.

"This one is skin and bones!" shouts a voice from the deck. The voice's owner peers over a rusty red railing, one hand holding the net, the other waving. A few easy strokes of his arms hoist me above deck. Although still confined to the belly of the oddly specific net, I am now face-to-face with its owner.

"Are you the casting director?"

The surprised casting director stares unblinkingly at his catch.

"I was Linus Number Two, you know." The wind whistles through the man's thick black beard, but it refuses to jiggle.

"Yes, I know," he says with a smile as he carefully releases me from the net. Flashing images of socially awkward stars, uncompassionate waves, and characters from Schulz's *Peanuts* fill my soggy skull as the afternoon's bright light fades to black.

A splitting pain reverberates though my temples—a sharp, angular sensation, which forces my wrinkled hand to my charred forehead. The pain shoots from one side of my skull to the other, like a pin on a pendulum alternatively pricking each side of my brain. Fatigue overwhelms me. It's as if every muscle in my body is slowly slipping from bones too tired to hold on, freely sliding around pockets of sagging skin.

I manage to sit up against one of the oak planks lining the perimeter of the room. Although a foggy gunk had welled up in my eyes, I am able to make out some of my surroundings. A large mahogany desk covered with maps dominates the room, while a dark leather armchair sits in the corner, next to an end table littered with tobacco. An intimidatingly wide hammock sways gently in the back of the room above my head. I have never been here before.

Panic swiftly takes over my senses. Gulping quick gasps of air, I search through my memory for any clue, any hint, as to how I managed to end up here. A deep weight sinks into my chest, and fear begins to distort my vision. The walls gently warp inward. I take slow, deep breaths and regroup—where is my familiar world?

A sturdy man with a thick black beard enters through the door, swaying gently as he walks toward the desk. He leans over it, squinting slightly as he traces imaginary lines on a map, pausing frequently to scratch the great mass of hair on his chin. He studies the markings without acknowledging my presence, mumbling softly to himself.

After ridding the foggy gunk from my eyes, my vision has now come completely into focus, but it is still difficult to see. The wooden window shades compress incoming rays of sunlight through tiny parallel slats, softly suffocating the room in its shadow. However, the man doesn't seem to mind the lack of light, studying the map with increased concentration. His dark pea coat and black slacks make his body blend in with the darkness, his pale face hovering like an apparition.

"Where do you think you are?" His deep voice deadens quickly against the oak siding. His eyes remain locked on the map.

"Where do I think I am?" The dry hissing words startle me—was that really my voice? The bearded man looks up and smiles, tilting the small canyons of wrinkles around his mouth.

"Doesn't it matter where you *think* you are? Understanding perspective is crucial for context, and context is crucial for understanding. So, I ask again, where do you think you are?" The man turns toward me, and leans against the desk as silence ensues, his eyes hidden in the shadow of his brow.

"I think I am in a dimly lit room"—I attempt to salivate, but to no avail—"in the company of a stranger."

"A *stranger?*" The man paces slowly toward the leather chair. "I am hardly a stranger. Unfamiliar, maybe, but I know quite a bit about you." He produces a wooden pipe from his pea coat as he sits down and crosses his legs.

"Who are you?"

He puts the pipe to his mouth, fishing something from his coat. With a quick flip of the wrist, the warm glow of a match lights up his face.

"My name is Roland Bracket, captain of the *Charoncross*." Quick bursts of smoke escape from his mouth, hovering around his head like a veil. "I will take you to your destination."

"We're on a boat? Where am I? Where are you taking me?" I can barely speak. Somehow I know I am never going home.

"We are going to the border." The captain slowly stands up and walks toward the window. "I think the shades are no longer necessary." He peeks though a slat and, satisfied, pulls them up in one fluid motion.

"The *border*? What is that?" Then instantly, I am silenced by the sunset—there is comfort in it. My breaths become even, and the grip of panic loosens from my chest. The incoming orange light reveals hanging clouds of smoke above the leather chair, trailing to the pipe still hanging from the captain's mouth.

"The border is a conclusion." The captain remains by the window, gazing intently at the sinking sun. He turns toward me, and takes the pipe from his mouth. "There is the matter of my fee."

"Fee?"

The captain chuckles as he approaches. He bends down, his face draws near; his tobacco-stained teeth form a smile. He grabs my jaw, pulls it down quickly, and inspects the inside of my mouth. He squints, but does not see what he is looking for. On his knees, he takes hold of my right hand. It limply unfolds, revealing the gold coin. The captain takes the coin with a smile and stands up.

"Thank you, sir." He begins walking toward the desk.

"Why are you doing this?"

The captain opens a drawer and flips the coin in. It lands with a clink.

"*This* is my job. *This* is my life. The sea is my country, and the *Charoncross* is my home. I know my place in the natural order of things, and it is here. Do you know your place?"

I am looking at my hands; I don't know what the captain wants to hear.

"Where are you *from*?" The captain sits back on the leather chair and reignites the pipe's ember. Though the windows are open, his face becomes dark—the light is fading rapidly now.

"I thought you knew me."

"Ah, but it is all about perspective. Where do you *think* you are from?" Smoke seeps out of his mouth as he grins.

The captain is toying with me. I am his plaything. An anger wells up in my stomach. I am breaking. What does this man want with me?

"Where do you think *you* are from?" My shaking voice doesn't startle the captain. He stares at me, taking a long draw from his pipe.

"I am from where all life is from—the water." The captain is not smiling. A shadow quickly descends upon his body. "The ocean is the mother of man, we are all her children."

"What are you talking about?" Emotion weaves into my words. I can feel my arms tremble under the blanket. I refuse to play his game.

"You and I are not so different—our bodies are made up of the same things. The ocean made us out of water . . . and to think some people are actually scared of the sea." He chuckles, but the laughter quickly becomes a hacking cough. The captain struggles to regain his composure, thick phlegm rising from his lungs. His head leaves the shadows of the corner, and his face reveals the intensity of the wheezing cough. He takes a few deep breaths, puts the pipe back in his mouth, and returns to the shadow.

"We are simply sacks of water, aimlessly walking around." He sighs and clears his throat. I am beginning to sense that the captain is no captor. He rises from the chair and returns to the window.

"Take a look."

I cannot stand. He walks over to me, and puts his hands under my armpits, and lifts me up. He carries my limp body to the window.

The sun is drowning in the sea, its rays screaming silently as the water claims it completely. Darkness encompasses the horizon, swallowing up the scenery in seconds. The ship, however, is not moving. The dark water sloshes rhythmically against the hull—had we been moving at all?

"We are getting close." The captain sets me on the leather chair. I can feel how the grooves in the cushion fit to his body.

"How can we be getting close if we aren't moving?"

As if he had anticipated my question, the captain smiles. "We were moving toward your destination for a while, but now it is moving toward us." The darkness outside grows to a deeper shade of black. The captain draws the shades, and the room instantly lights up.

"So, where are we exactly?" The grip of panic sets its claws into my stomach once again. We could be anywhere.

"Let me respond to your question with another question: What is your first memory?"

I don't know what to say—is he serious? The curiosity in his eyes appears authentic; he sits attentively, waiting for a response. I cannot think straight. Signals in my brain seem to fire at random. My experiences are lost within me. Then, without warning, the memory comes into focus.

"I am opening the door to the living room. There are clothes piled on the floor. My mother is folding a shirt. She smiles at me. The carpet is tan. She motions for me to come toward her. Her shirt is faded blue. I don't move. There are large white button-up shirts on the table. She isn't smiling anymore. Her belly is round with my brother."

"Where are you?"

"I am in the house where I grew up. I am standing there, in the living room."

"That is your first memory?" asks the captain as he picks up his pipe from the end table.

"Yes, but why does it matter?"

The captain grabs tobacco from a desk drawer and sprinkles it in the pipe. He walks toward the door, and turns toward me.

"Bookends."

He flings open the door; darkness rushes into the room, black waves wash over us. I can't breathe; I am drowning in the shadows. A match reveals the captain's face in the doorway as he lights his pipe. The tobacco burns easily, and its glow approaches the armchair. The captain picks me up and carries me through the doorway. The burning tobacco is all that is visible; there is no moon. The water is completely calm; it no longer sloshes against the hull. Silence.

"This is as far as I can take you." His voice is mechanic, as if reading from a script.

I am powerless, and it is comforting. There is no panic in my chest, there are no questions racing through my skull, there is only the captain and the silent sea. Then I see her. She is standing next to a pile of clothes, smiling at me. The captain sets me down on the deck. Her shirt is faded blue. She drops the shirt, her belly round with my brother. He puts me in his net. I am standing there, in the living room. She motions for me to come to her. He lowers me down to the water. She is still smiling. The water is not fluid. There are large white button-up shirts on the table. The net is gone. I am standing. Her arms are open. There is no boat; there is no room; there is no pain. With all my strength, with all my love, I run to her.

||

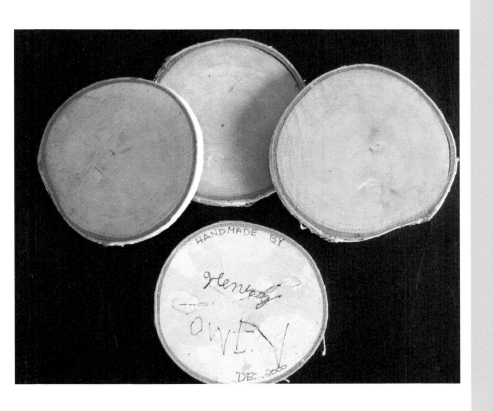

Henry Mackaman loved to read books. There are some books that go on and on, like the ones James Michener wrote, that start at the beginning of time and end . . . long after I stopped reading. I gotta admit, I could never get to the end of one of those books.

Maybe that's why I believe the best stories are short. The ones where the author has to work really hard to cram a lifetime of living, loving, music, adventure, travels, and friendships . . . into just a handful of pages . . . that you'll never forget.

Dan Mackaman
Henry's Uncle

LONGER TOGETHER

Iron eyes rusted shut,
pried open to the morning's call.
She glides back into our feathered world,
where we hid from the moon's judgment gaze.
Her skin sparkles to my touch,
lips like peppermint
caress my eager cheek.
The jealous sun calls for attention,
but we'll shut the blinds
and stay hidden
for a moment
longer together.

TOM COPPER'S WAX GRAVEYARD

"Ready for the first read-through, Ron?"

He paced along the perimeter of the drawing room, avoiding the angular leather couch pushed up against the wall. Ron was good at avoiding obstacles—it was his job.

The leather couch, like all the furniture in the apartment, was completely new. He had needed a fresh start, so he paid a mousy woman named Moreen to decorate the place, and after a week at the Hilton, he had finally moved back in that morning. Ron looked at her work as he walked out of the drawing room and into the den. A blank check buys a lot: French light fixtures nearly a century old, confusing and dark paintings, an Italian smoking chair—all placed to give off the air of what Moreen called "fashionable despair."

"Fashionable despair," he said, pulling a cigar out of a familiar end table. Ron sat down on the Italian smoking chair and decided it was terribly uncomfortable.

Grunting, he stood up and walked to the entrance of the drawing room. The documents were in a manila envelope on the old oak desk—he could see them from the doorway. He sighed and retrieved matches from his breast pocket. He lit the cigar, tossed the jacket onto the leather couch, and put the matches in his pocket.

The floorboards creaked under the burgundy carpet as he walked toward the desk and reached for the folder, puffing the cigar at regular intervals. Tom's testimony was heavy in his hands. He turned on the reading light next to the leather couch, opened the folder, and sat down. He found the couch terribly uncomfortable.

He read, "I am guilty of no more than curiosity and capitalism—the very capitalist idea that this country was founded on. I am no criminal; I am an entrepreneur, and I have my rights. I have no doubt that the media is to blame for the sharp stares and foul words that I have come to receive. Why must the masses fear innovation and industry? Why must their tongues sing spikes of hatred into my heart? No, I am not so guilty as I am misunderstood. People look at me like an executioner, but I am a mortician. I do as I am told—where there is demand, there is supply. Yes, I am merely the supplier, so why must I suffer for the demands that I satisfy? I am not a criminal; I am not guilty. I will show all of this to you, and by the tears of Morrissey, I pray you will see the light of truth—for it is 'a light that never goes out.'"

Ron had to stand up. He looked at the leather couch in contempt—how could something so expensive feel so much like cold concrete? The cigar was hitting the sweet spot as Ron, manila folder in hand, left the drawing room once again. The Italian smoking chair seemed to mock him as he passed, and he glared at it as he placed the cigar in his mouth and took the top off of an ornate glass whiskey decanter.

The sound of the whiskey splashing into the glass rose higher in pitch and thinner in tone until the whiskey overflowed onto the table. Ron broke his gaze with the chair and cursed as he scrambled to find a rag. All the kitchen cabinets were empty, and the oven handle bare. Ron ran back to the spill and began to mop up the floor with his argyle sock, cursing wildly. He then turned his attention to the tabletop, using his other sock to sop up the outlandishly expensive concoction. He threw the soaked socks into the kitchen and retrieved the brimming glass of whiskey from the table. He put out the cigar, picked up the manila folder, and walked into his bedroom.

Ron smiled at the plush green armchair in the corner opposite the bed—it looked much more comfortable than its predecessors. The whole bedroom was green. "It's the calming color," Moreen had explained. Ron noticed that he did feel a slight sense of calm as he sank into the armchair and opened up the folder.

"When the body dies, the music of the soul lives on—and what better way to symbolize this effect than to press one's ashes into a vinyl record? It's the logical conclusion for any music fan—why, you could literally be one with the music! The idea struck me two years ago when I, thinking the dark and lofty thoughts of a lonely mind, turned to the medicine of music. I was listening to "Black Sabbath" (the song by the group of the same name) when I realized that I would die into nothingness, uselessness. But then something wonderful happened— the needle of my record player caught a rough series of grooves and began to create a crackle and hiss over the song. By sweet Morrissey's howl it sounded like a fire— but not just any fire, a funeral pyre. The image compelled me.

"I hatched my plan. My friend Franz set up the website while I procured the necessary materials to make a record. It was not easy. Making a record requires many steps and many machines, but my father worked at Garden Record Plant for fifteen years and agreed to help. With my father's guidance, I leased the plant's old machines and began to make test pressings. I pressed Marvin Gaye, Steve Miller, and Depeche Mode to hone my skills. I succeeded. The site went live two months later, and we had our first order within two weeks.

"His name was Hans Maccabee, and he died in a car crash in Vermont. He was nineteen years old. The Maccabees called me two weeks after their son's death— they wanted his ashes pressed into his favorite record, Joy Division's *Unknown Pleasures*. It should be known that I am not a Joy Division fan (save for their 1979 *The Peel Sessions*), but I do understand their impact and influence. The Maccabees agreed to my terms, and the pressing began. Hans's ashes came in a small box. I was sure to mix them carefully with the vinyl pellets I had procured, and I decided to make three presses and send off the record that sounded best. The first press was a failure. The ashes overpowered the vinyl itself, and the result was constant crackling. I thought I got it right the second time. The record sounded great at first, but it was during the first verse of the sixth song, 'She's Lost Control,' that I made the awful discovery that today brings ruin to my name."

Ron couldn't put up with the squishy green armchair anymore. He stood up cursing, slapping the testimony against his hip. The warmth from the whiskey and the calming nature of the green wallpaper set his boiling blood to rest with a few deep breaths. The charges made Tom Copper look like a lunatic, a psychopath, but he had money—at least enough to pay for a defense lawyer of Ron's caliber. His reputation for getting clients out of jams had won him fame and fortune, but the case of Tom Copper's Wax Graveyard was like nothing he had ever seen. He finished off the whiskey. *Where to begin?* Ron paused before deciding that procuring more whiskey and finding a suitable chair was a good start.

Replenished whiskey in hand, he passed the kitchen and walked to the dining room. This was where he would entertain guests if he ever decided to do so, but he was tired of condolences and pity. The table was made of zinc, and the chairs surrounding it were of modern British design. They looked as if they couldn't support the weight of a basketball, let alone a full-grown man. "The integration of modern design into a fundamentally classic layout is all the rage in New York," Moreen had said behind her half-moon glasses. Ron had been to New York several times for work and he found it very dirty. New Orleans was dirty, too, but at least it had charm.

Ron sat down in the foreign chair. It leaned a little to the left, but Ron found it to be surprisingly comfortable. He took another swig of whiskey and opened up the testimony.

"I heard Hans's ashes. They wisped over Ian Curtis' vocals like a faint wind, but the wind became stronger and stronger. Suddenly, the vocals cut out all together, and I swear by sweet Morrissey's quiff that I heard the dead boy speak through the grooves: *'If I must die, I will comply . . . If only I could tell her . . . Those unknown pleasures escape me . . .'* Wide-eyed in confused agony, I listened over and over to his words. Yes, I heard them, I know I heard them! I listened to the rest of the record, but the voice did not return.

"How could this have happened? How might this record come to traverse the divide between the living and dead, and I, the puppet of its creation? I decided to press a third record with the remainder of the ashes, in an attempt to repeat the experiment. I listened to the product, and sure enough, the voice appeared once more, this time on the second track, 'Day of Lords.' It gave the same message as before. What had I done?

"I had no choice—I sent the Maccabees the second record. The first was ruined, and the voice appeared earlier on the third. To this day I do not know if they ever listened to it. I do know that they paid dearly for it. My fee had been paid in full, but I needed more orders to pay off the equipment I had leased from the record plant. I was trapped in the business. Of course, I was terrified of the voice I had heard, but at this point I had convinced myself it was a fluke, or that maybe it was my own poor mind playing tricks on its keeper. There are always other explanations for what the mind refuses to accept.

"Meanwhile, the website had garnered attention from several blogs in the realms of music and curiosity, and overnight, Tom Copper's Wax Graveyard became an Internet sensation. I received emails requesting interviews and pictures, but I was torn—publicity is good for business, but at the time I had decided to make my investment back and get out of the record business. My low profile only increased interest—curiosity gets the better of men, and I was curious too. What else might I uncover?

"The second and third requests came in rapid succession—an unofficial Grateful Dead roadie named Barry, and a disc jockey named Leo. I started with the latter, as I don't much care for the Dead. Leo had died of lung cancer at the age of sixty-four, and he requested to be pressed into Nick Drake's *Pink Moon*. I am quite a Nick Drake fan—I'll never forget the first time I heard "From the Morning," lonely and stoned in a college apartment. Good choice, Leo.

"I again decided to make three presses, separating the ashes into equal lumps next to the vinyl pellets. I anxiously awaited the first press and listened to it as soon as it was complete. The grooves played smoothly up until the sixth track, "Things Behind the Sun." The words of the dead man came through loud and clear: 'So . . . uh . . . this is it, eh? . . . Well . . . guess I'll find out what the winning religion is . . . Wait . . . What . . . Is that Morrissey?'

"I had done it again! It was no fluke! I had devised a one-way line to the thoughts of the dead! Feeling validated, I convinced myself my discovery was a blessing, not a curse. I should've stopped there, but a question beckoned in the back of my mind. Like many men, I have lost both friends and lovers in my lifetime, but I alone could bring them back."

The chair's spine snapped and Ron toppled onto the floor. The whiskey numbed some of the pain shooting through his shoulder, but the acute pricks of agony forced great groans from his lips. Ron shifted onto his back and lay still on the floor. He stretched his limbs, took a deep breath, and stared at the ceiling.

"This is not my beautiful house," he said to the empty whiskey glass by his side. The whiskey glass looked at the talking head in silence. Ron sat up, and the room began to spin. It was as if he had broken into someone else's life and drank all of their whiskey. He wished he could've walked into a life less lonely. *It didn't always used to be this way*, he thought, staring at the mantle. He stood up, using the zinc table for support. The table proved to be much sturdier than the chair. Ron grabbed the testimony from the tabletop and walked toward the mantle. She was there, in a picture, next to a small sculpture of a human figure. Ron looked at her, and then at Tom's testimony.

"My Wax Graveyard grew, and I had to get help. I taught Franz how to press records, and we soon employed several other friends to process orders and work through licensing loopholes. More importantly, though, the secret was out; people heard the whispers in the grooves. Some thought the voices were overdubbed while others believed we had Satan on our side. It didn't matter what people thought—we weren't saying anything, and we were making money.

"All the while my curiosity grew—how could it not? If you had a gift, would you not use it? All the misery I had suffered through—how many times I had relived that horrible October day! How many dreams I've had hunched over the phone in my old flat! How suddenly she was gone! My mind was made up. Oh, but how I regret what I did! The mental torture of digging amongst peaceful graves under the watchful moon, overridden by a mixture of curiosity and hope. Still, I had to know; I had to do it. What message had she for me?

"I paid to have her remains cremated after hours at a shady clinic on the edge of New Orleans. A balding skeleton of a man took my money and gave me a small box. By Morrissey's blue eyes, I'll never forget that feeling—how surreal his smile was as he handed it to me! I brought her to my makeshift factory. It was well past midnight when I finished the plates for My Bloody Valentine's *Loveless*—Heather's favorite record. I separated her ashes in the usual way, three equal clumps next to three heaps of vinyl pellets. I made the first press in a blur and held the record in my hands, mystified. The time for answers had come."

Ron threw the testimony to the floor and held his head in his hands. It was midnight, and a fierce and driving wind rattled the curtain violently. Ron stumbled to the window, the strong gusts driving his brown bangs from his face. He shut it as a torrential rain began to pound against the roof. Whiskey and disbelief swirled in his veins as he sat down beneath the window, eyeing the testimony from afar.

"It can't be . . .", he said as the power went out.
Ron crawled toward the papers, feeling blindly for them. He stopped, remembering the matches in his pocket. The tiny flame illuminated the floor, and Ron hastily grabbed the testimony, flipping to the last page.

"I put the record on the player and carefully

put the needle on the vinyl. The grooves came to life when the drums knocked the band into the first song, 'Only Shallow.' The distorted sounds filled my factory. Although the clock read three in the morning, I turned my speakers all the way up. The crackle of her ashes sparked above the tune every once in a while, but no voice materialized. I listened through the first six songs in this way, imagining hearing her words in my sleep-deprived state. Then, finally, in the middle of the seventh track, 'Come In Alone,' I heard her voice: *I have to do this . . . for me . . . I'm sorry, Dad . . .*"

The flame died as Ron collapsed into the darkness.

||

"

When I'm a ghost
I see no reason to run
When I'm already gone
If it wasn't taped, you
could escape this song
But I'm already gone

-"Jesus Fever," Kurt Vile

Song played April 5, 2011 on
The Grooving Tree.

Song played again on
April 12, 2011.

"

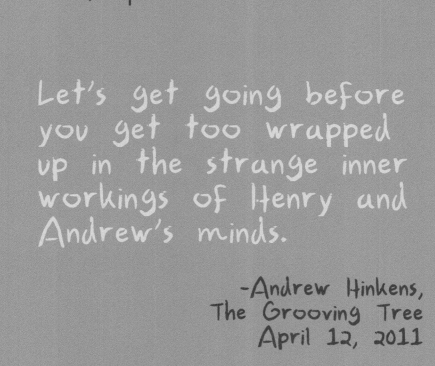

Let's get going before
you get too wrapped
up in the strange inner
workings of Henry and
Andrew's minds.

-Andrew Hinkens,
The Grooving Tree
     April 12, 2011

MIDWEST-CENTRIC GOOD VIBRATIONS

by **KEVIN KOUSHA** ⊠**Nov 21, 2011**
Originally published in *The Badger Herald*

Musical taste has become quite the political matter.

Music snobbery is often viewed with disdain, but many still pass judgment on the listening of others. People often fret to find bands still mired in obscurity, to discover genres on the upswing and musical pioneers and, of course, to have staple local bands.

This can all be a taxing ordeal. Bands often become famous because their music is universally liked; they often shed their "local" label when they gain enough notoriety. The hunt is endless, and with so many performing hopefuls, often quite difficult. But with enough digging, gems can be found.

Such is the case with Phantom Vibration. Primarily based out of St. Paul, Minn., the band has a connection to Madison through member Henry Mackaman, a sophomore at the University of Wisconsin.

Mackaman formed the band with Dan Clinton-McCausland in their senior year of high school, "as a means to pass time in our econ class," Mackaman recounted. The pair would "listen to Nico and talk about music in the back row." While this may not be the most conventional way to kill time, the end result was the formation of Phantom Vibration, and the pair has been playing together ever since.

Recently, Gunnar Kauth became the group's newest member, adding depth to their sound. Though Mackaman is a UW student, his two counterparts are in school in Minnesota. This distance proves the largest obstacle for the three. Regardless, they aren't swayed and have continued to push forward. Their first EP was released before the band played with Kauth, and they spent last summer working on their live performance as a trio.

Even so, Mackaman admitted that "mixing and mastering our EPs has been a huge pain," and the band relies on emails to get the process done. Especially for new bands with little funds or experience, producing quality recordings is often a huge obstacle. Still, the members of Phantom Vibration have managed to produce two professional-sounding EPs.

Booking shows has been another issue due to distance. While they have played together since the summer, some portion of the band has to make the journey from one state to the other. "I'm getting pretty familiar with the Megabus," Mackaman said.

The band has a sort of musical equivalent to a long distance relationship, and they face similar issues to one. But it's clear, through their recordings, that they're making it work.

Phantom Vibration released their first EP, *Kids*, in March, and recently released their second, *Growing*. Their final EP, *Aged*, will complete the set. Mackaman reinforced what the titles suggest, saying that "Each EP is a snapshot of a different stage of life."

To be sure, the band aimed for a different sound in their second EP than their first, showing off the breadth of their ability. Also, perhaps less intentionally, the band has matured musically, just as their EPs have thematically. All of the musical promise to be heard in *Kids* is fulfilled in *Growing*.

All of Phantom Vibration's songs are still musically unified, and the band has a distinct and consistent sound, something Mackaman dubbed "a dreamy aesthetic." To be sure, their tracks are rife with high sounds like organs and bells, along with a certain low-fi sound that matches the band's musical sound well.

This style complements the motif of their EP concept perfectly, creating a dream-like haze over the tracks, like the memories of childhood they try to capture.

Mackaman cites his own influences as bands like The Black Keys and Television, and McCausland cites The Decemberists and Fleet Foxes. More of the latter can be heard in Phantom Vibration's sound. "We are big fans of warm glowy vibes," Mackaman explained, something that has to be heard to be fully understood.

Currently, Mackaman and the rest of Phantom Vibration have their sights set on finishing their EP concept with *Aged*. Beyond that, they're both unsure and excited. On the topic, Mackaman remarked simply, "We'll see where it goes."

More information about Phantom Vibration can be found at http://phantomvibration.bandcamp.com.

||

SUMMER BLOOD

Phantom Vibration

Summer seeps silently into my blood
But in many ways I fear the days that have gone.

But I won't worry myself.
The active years are few.
But I've been searching so long,
So much left to do,
so much left to do,
ooh—so much left to do.

Few harsh words from a mouth are all I can take,
Boots to the grind, til there's no time left to waste.

But I won't hurry myself,
The active years are gone.
It's all been so easy
Since I let myself go myself go.

So let yourself go
Ooh—let yourself go.

Heartache comes in different forms don't you think?
Beauty lies to the eyes of the mind on the brink.
But I will find an answer.
Scale the cliff's broad smile
Or maybe chop the mountain down,
Or maybe go crazy for a while
So let's go crazy for a while
Ooh—crazy for a while.

So let the shimmering sun start raising your blood like
the tide,
Your restless mind too proud to confide in a smile.
Maybe go crazy for a while
Yes, maybe things go crazy for a while . . .

"

Henry's nickname Shig came from
when the boys were little.

When we were getting ready to
go somewhere, they had to get
their shoes. Henry was Big Shoe
and Owen was Little Shoe.

Big Shoe quickly reversed
to Shig Boo.
And then came Shiggy.
And then just Shig.

Meredith Leigh,
Henry's mom

"

THE SHIG

a guitar that Henry
built by hand.

JOE HUBERT'S LES PAUL STANDARD

The Hubert family's Volvo station wagon rolled into the Sunnyville Senior residency to the fanfare of an afternoon thunderstorm. Clouds had consumed any and all traces of the July blue sky even before Mrs. Hubert poured herself the glass of water necessary to take with her medicine. The youngest Hubert brother, Arnold, always insisted that he was present for his mother's morning ritual, but he didn't know that the little yellow pills hid under his mother's tongue only long enough to appease him.

The eldest Hubert brother, Bradford, tended to the python hidden in the crawl space above his closet during his brother's daily absence from their shared room, and he fed the growing serpent cat food and lunch meat stolen from the pantry. Mr. Hubert stretched out in his den while sipping black Colombian coffee to the searing sounds of Charlie Parker, unaware that his son's pet lurked directly under the floorboards of his weathered chair. The Huberts, like any family, had a routine, and their individual morning meanderings ended at exactly 9:00 a.m. every Sunday, because Sunday was dedicated to visiting Grandpa Joe.

A nurse with stumpy legs and an eerily arched back greeted the family through Sunnyville's entrance with a cloud of cigarette smoke and a smile. She had worked there ever since Joe first arrived after the stroke, and she knew the Huberts fairly well for never having had a conversation with them. Joe had told her stories—everyone had told her stories. They were always the same. Each resident had five or six that made the daily conversational rounds, and she knew them all by heart. She watched the Huberts walk down the hall to Joe's room as she brought the cigarette back to her lips and sucked.

"Would you believe that nurse is always smoking

whenever we come here?" said Mr. Hubert to his wife. Mrs. Hubert nodded and looked into an empty room to her right. She saw a small black cross on the otherwise bare beige walls as she passed.

"It's ridiculous—I mean, what do they teach in nursing school these days?" This made Mr. Hubert feel better about himself. He often thought of his jazz record collection and his knowledge of coffee when he questioned the worth of himself or others.

"Charlie Parker is the only addiction a man needs!" he said with a smile.

"Charlie Parker was a junkie," replied Mrs. Hubert coldly as the family arrived outside Joe's room.

Mr. Hubert hadn't seemed to hear his wife, and he swiftly knocked on the door with a standard polyrhythm spiced up with a spurt of triplets. Joe never answered the door, but Mr. Hubert always made a point of showing off his high school jazz drummer chops.

Bradford and Arnold led the way into the room and jostled for the chance to play the 1956 Gibson Les Paul Standard that sat quietly in the corner of the room. Joe had bought the guitar with the advance of his band's first record, and kept it by his side for every world tour and recording session that came his way. Bradford grabbed the guitar from its stand and slung the strap over his neck. Arnold gripped the guitar's front horn and pulled, causing the strap to break from the back of the neck. The guitar came tumbling down and landed with a sharp thud.

Joe looked at the boys and wondered if they were truly related to him. If he were younger he would've thrown a fit, but the stroke had left the right side of his body useless. The guitar he had treated better than his mother was now an ornament in the room he would die in. Even so, he never let it out of his sight.

"I'm sorry about that, Pop," said the red-faced Mr. Hubert. Bradford and Arnold stood paralyzed behind their mother.

"Did I ever tell you how I got that guitar?" asked Joe softly. Mr. Hubert looked at his wife apologetically.

"An AR from Electra Records was down at the

Whisky a Go Go to catch one of the Doors' earliest shows opening for my buddy Arthur Lee's band, Love. Well, Arthur got the stomach flu and offered the slot to my band, and we took it." Joe coughed, and Mr. Hubert checked his watch.

"The Electra rep signed both of us the same night, and I bought that Les Paul first thing in the morning." Joe laughed and smiled at the thought of sitting across the table from Jim Morrison.

"Grab that old guitar, won't you, Jim?" Mr. Hubert looked at his father gravely as he knelt down and returned, offering up the splintered pieces of the instrument.

Joe felt a jolt of pain down his left arm and his lungs seemed to cave in. He reached for the remote call button attached to a necklace the nurses forced him to wear. He had always hated the thing (he called it his death button) and he pressed it with all his might.

The formerly smoking nurse rushed in and quickly examined his vitals. Joe extended his arm toward his son, and Jim quickly put down the pieces of the guitar and grasped his father's left hand. He quickly lost his grip as Joe continued to flail his mobile limb. Mrs. Hubert pushed her boys toward their grandfather, but Joe waved them off, too. The nurse calmly knelt down and picked up the pieces of the Les Paul. She placed the neck in Joe's hand. His grip tightened until his fingers turned white. The Hubert family looked on in horror as the guitar fell back on the floor with a familiar thud.

||

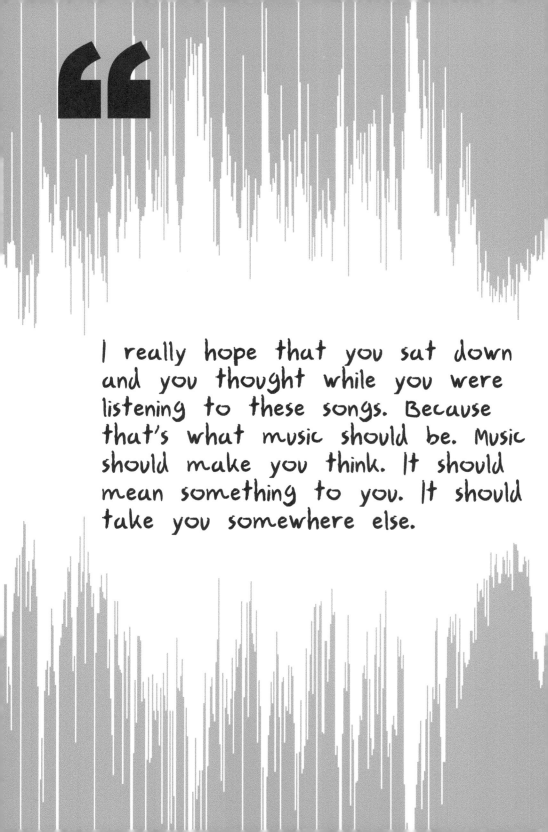

I really hope that you sat down and you thought while you were listening to these songs. Because that's what music should be. Music should make you think. It should mean something to you. It should take you somewhere else.

Music is merely a vessel for your mind to go off into space. Your imagination.

-Henry, The Grooving Tree
May 3, 2011 After playing
"Blue Spotted Tail," "Blowin' in the Wind,"
"Castles Made of Sand," and "Alter Ego."

PORCH LIGHT

By Lisa Heyman, in memory of
Henry Mackaman and Tamar Kaplan

Screen door
Bare feet
Loons wail
Stars are spreading

Screen door
Bare feet
Loons wail
Stars are spreading
We leave the porch light on for you

Laughter echoes
Moonlight shines, river flows
Your songs are always playing

Laughter echoes
Moonlight shines, river flows
Your songs are always playing
We leave the porch light on for you

770·100.7·104.5
AM   FM
RADIO K
©LEAH GARAAS

I would say that I wish you
were here, but you are.

You are everywhere, Henry,
in the beautiful house that you
found for all of us.

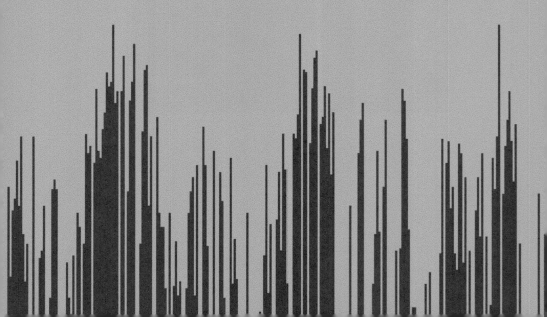

I wish we could speak to you
through more than just your
picture on the mantelpiece, but
we have your music for that,
and your soul.

Love you always and
forever, Henry. Always.

Ola Lisowski,
Henry's roommate
August 16, 2013

SAPIENCE

By Phantom Vibration

Eyes to the ceiling
we paid for this feeling
once again
vivid visions in sleepless beds
of approaching oblivion
there is nothing to be done, nothing to be done.

Ooo the end is coming soon
of countless nights spent staring at the moon,
and what it means today, well it's hard to say
Ooo you're a kid in a cocoon

What would you pay for
complacency
When all that you wait for
is endless sleep
what will you do
when all that you
dreamed is done?

Awake in a dark room
air hangs in a vacuum
could it be
the walls have broken free,
in a barren lucid dream

All the aimless games of
feigning ignorance have been erased
tiny floating scattered spheres
suspended are all that remain
then suddenly a wave of heat puts life into the clay
love is all of life together wandering through space

Ooo the end is coming soon
all you build today tomorrow will be ruins,
and when our debt is paid, lying in a grave
Ooo we'll be staring at the moon

What would you pay for
complacency
When all that you wait for
is endless sleep
what will you do
when all that you
dreamed is done?

"

There's no reason not
to be an organ donor.

It gives me a sense of
comfort and purpose to
know that, because of
Henry, someone else will
have a chance to write
a poem or a song.

-Meredith Leigh,
 Henry's mom

Henry was an organ donor, and that decision helped five people.

Walter Goodman, a professor at Henry's university, was his heart recipient.

On Thursday, I became certified as a Designated Requestor by UW Organ Procurement, meaning that I am now certified to ask family members in the most painful moments of their lives if their loved one would be an organ donor.

As a loving friend of an organ donor, this was both an easy choice and a difficult process. UW's OPO (organ procurement organization) allowed me to tour their offices, and I got to meet people so happy and willing to meet me, and so grateful for the gift Henry gave to so many other people. The most surreal part was talking to a social worker who had just been listening to the Phantom Vibration Bandcamp!

As we flow down the stream of life, we muddy the waters with our regrets. One of mine for a long time had been not being able to share a beer and talk with my friend.

But today, I'm sitting in a comfy chair, listening to "Sapience," and thinking of all the ways those we love find their way home to our hearts, no matter the distance.

How Henry still found a way, 3.5 years from his gift and turned away from the shared path of our lives, to wish me a happy birthday. And it finally makes cosmic sense.

Love endures all things.

Neal Cragg,
October 8, 2016

"

MY HEART WILL GO ON

Henry loved *Titanic*, the story of Jack and Rose and the tragic sinking of the magnificent boat. He loved it so much he and I ended up building a replica of the ship on our beach at Cedar Lake.

In a way the ship is a metaphor for Henry's life. They both came to early tragic ends. The Titanic's lifeboats saved many of the passengers, and Henry's vital organs saved the lives of several people, notably our friend Walter Goodman.

David Strand, Henry's grandpa

"This magazine was found on Henry's bedside table after he died."

THE COOL MORNING BREEZE CAUSED RIPPLES ATOP THE MURKY WATER. A SHIP LAY AT REST, TIED TO THE ANCIENT DOCK THAT CREAKED AND MOANED AS THE SUN APPROACHED IT. WORN AND DIRTY ROPES HELD THE SHIP IN PLACE, AS LONELY GULLS CRIED. SMALL FOOTSTEPS COULD BE HEARD THROUGHOUT DENMARK. IT WAS THE LATE 1890S. WEARY AND DESPERATE, THE CROWDS GATHERED. GREAT-GRANDMOTHER PUT HER NOSE INTO THE

AIR AND SMELLED THE SALTY OCEAN AS MANY BEFORE HER HAD DONE. SHE PEERED INTO THE SACK SHE HAULED AND SAW HER SENTIMENTAL VALUED ITEMS. GREAT-GRANDMOTHER'S FACE WORE A MIXED EXPRESSION AS SHE STEPPED ONTO THE OLD SHIP. JUST THEN, THE LONESOME HORN BLEW. THE ROPES WERE UNTIED, THE SHIP SET FREE, NOTHING MORE, ONLY HOPES HANGING IN THE AIR.

-Henry Ma. kaman, Published in the *StarTribune* March 7, 2005

RESTLESS WESTERN WINDS

Haunted by the slumber of the sea
so we swallowed salty water
as we sank into the deep.
She sat silent by the stony shore,
becoming the burden of her womb,
praying to a deafened god

that our boat would come home soon.

TWIN
BICYCLES

They met when she hit him and his bicycle

with the school's car while taking her driver's education course. She failed the course, but he fixed up a bicycle for her and they would ride across the town. Her curly brown hair blew behind her as they pedaled down to Piddler's Creek, away from where the rowdy kids dove off of tire swings and called each other names. There they could sit in peace and watch the river easily rumble by. There seemed to be no trouble in the world in those days.

When fall came and the trees began their vibrant showcasing of their annual deaths, the time for carelessness had past. She left her bicycle in her parents' garage when she went away. His bicycle never left his side and pedaled with him to college. There was not a day where he didn't ride his bicycle, hoping that somewhere she was riding hers. As more time passed, his tires grew weak, and his frame grew rusty. Each and every pedal was a challenge, but he nurtured its ailments and rode on for the rest of his education.

The home he returned to was not the home he left. The struggles of daily life dragged him down, and soon he had no time for his needy bicycle. She returned from school to a home she remembered fondly. It wasn't long before she found the old bike in her parents' garage, just the way she had left it (except dustier). She put her feet on the pedals and found nostalgia as her curly brown hair flew behind her. She pedaled all the way down to Piddler's Creek, but found that her once-favorite place was now a restaurant. She was disheartened by the change, but somehow felt pressured to enter the establishment. She was seated in a table for two by a young girl with a plastic smile. She ordered coffee. As her eyes wandered about the dismal interior she saw him. He seemed older, his hair was thin and there were bags around his eyes. He looked tired and beaten, far from the boy she had hit with the car so long ago. She put a five-dollar bill on the table and hurried out of the building. She cried on the way back to her parents' house. She had been looking forward for years to riding her bicycle, but now it just wasn't the same.

He returned home from a long shift at the restaurant and collapsed on the couch. "What's the point of living if you don't get to live?" he said aloud to no one. Although it was late, he went out to the garage. The bicycle was just where he had left it. He began his work immediately, and soon he had his bicycle in gleaming new condition. He began pedaling, slow at first, and then fast. He had never gone this fast before, but it felt great as the wind forced tears out of his eyes. He closed his eyes and took his hands off the bars. It wasn't long before he crashed.

His eyes were now wide open, and he stared into the parked car he had just run into. The old green car was dented, and the glass was broken. He had long scrapes up and down his arms, legs, and face. His bicycle, however, was perfectly intact, and glistened in the moonlight. He limped away as a light in a nearby house came on, his bicycle at his side. On his way home, he couldn't help but think of her.

She did not intend to stay in this unfamiliar town. The harsh reality of things slapped her across the face and told her to leave. "What's the point of staying if there's nothing to stay for?" she said aloud to no one. She went outside to find her old green car broken into. Unfazed, she turned the key and began moving, slow at first, and then fast. She had never gone this fast before, and she sobbed as the motor easily rumbled along. She closed her eyes and took her hands off the wheel. It wasn't long before she crashed. They say his bicycle was perfectly intact.

CALLOUSED HANDS

Calloused hands grip broken glass
Bitter blood under the overpass
I hang my head;
The day is done
Settled dust cradles
The sleeping sun
Who knows what's best
For me?
My numbered days
Spent so lonely
Through the windshield I fly
Why are you so sad?

EVERYTHING

Walking out upon the lake,
I looked beneath my feet and thought
I want to know everything
But with every stranger,
Every distant planet,
Every look you gave me,
Teary-eyed and baffled,
Every path engraved in snow
I wonder and decide
I can only know myself.

"

Be safe on your
bicycles,

because it is such a
great day and I have
a feeling the weather
is only going to get
better.

So get out on your bicycle and go out and explore the world,

but be safe while you're doing so.

Henry,
The Grooving Tree
February 6, 2012

HENRY'S SHOES SHOW THE WEAR FROM HIS PREFERRED FORM OF TRANSPORTA-TION⊠ HIS LONGBOARD.

"I HAD THIS CRAZY DREAM LAST NIGHT WHEREIN MGMT PLAYED A SHOW IN FRONT OF A FRAT HOUSE. AND ANDREW, MY ROOMMATE NICK, AND MYSELF CAMPED OUT IN FRONT OF THIS FRAT HOUSE TO SEE MGMT. AND AT ONE POINT IN THE SHOW THEY THREW ALL THESE BOUNCY BALLS UP IN THE AIR AND I WAS TRYING TO CATCH ONE. BUT THEN THIS BIG DUDE WITH DREADLOCKS CAME AND CAUGHT THE BOUNCY BALL RIGHT BEFORE I WAS GOING TO CATCH IT AND I WAS REALLY PISSED. AND THEN I WAS WALKING TO CLASS TODAY WITH THIS GIRL HALEY AND ALL OF A SUDDEN I SEE THIS DREADLOCKED MAN. I KNOW, I KNOW! HE WAS GETTING ON HIS MOPED."

"LADIES AND GENTLEMEN OF THE AUDIENCE, YOU CAN'T SEE MY FACE RIGHT NOW, BUT IT IS A LOOK OF UTTER SHOCK AND AWE."

"CAN YOU IMAGINE MY FACE THOUGH? I WAS FLIPPING SHIT. I WAS FLIPPING SOME SERIOUS SHIT. BECAUSE I LOOKED AT THIS GUY AND WE MADE EYE CONTACT FOR A SOLID SECOND AND THEN, LIKE, I LOOKED AWAY AND I EXPLAINED TO HALEY THE SITUATION. I LOOKED BACK AND HE WAS STILL LOOKING AT ME. WHICH PROMPTED ME TO THINK THAT, PERHAPS, JUST PERHAPS, I WAS IN HIS DREAM.

I KNOW. TAKE IT IN."

-Henry and Andrew Hinkens, *The Grooving Tree*, April 5, 2011

Warm cinnamon
Sweet ~~simple~~ November Maple
familiar
i don't, much time to live
have
I'm afraid, its just that simple

I WAS DEAD BEFORE I WAS BORN

Our tale is not one of
luck, chance, or fate,
only of what is
and what will be.
Self-advancing technology
constantly adapting, developing,
serving our being
to the best of our ability.
However,
these decisions are not our own.
Free will is not free.
Everything has already been decided.
My genetics made the face I see in the mirror.
My environment made the voice in my head
dictating every action,
every trigger, every caress, every tear,
every smoking inhale.
Our path is set.
There is no room for luck, chance, or fee.
There's only what is, and what will be.

REINCAR= NATION

Is this heaven?
Where am I?
What am I?
Hmm, a pool of water . . .
Ah, I must have been a beautiful fountain!
So all my good deeds have paid off.
Now I will firmly stand
as a symbol of peace and prosperity.
Come throw pennies
into my elegant porcelain!
Perhaps I can grant wishes!
What a wonderful existence.
Ah, and here comes my first visitor.
Come stranger,
throw me coins, relax, and be merry!
That's it, grab the newspaper,
become an informed citizen of the world.
Why must you act so strangely?
Ahh! What the . . .
Is that an ass?
Come no closer!

Hello future self!

Hows life going? I hope you're pretty cool, and not dead. That would really suck. If I am dead, I hope I died in an interesting way, like falling down a bottomless pit or something like that.

So the assignment...

1. Remember that even little actions can easily become a big deal. Just put your mind to it.

2. Don't waste water, because then Chuck Norris will kill many a kitten. Do you remember that? If not, then you wont get that joke.

3. Preserve the lake. Keep it clean, spread the word.

Now for the fun stuff.

Hows guituring coming along? you better be practicing everyday, because if not my future self is lame. Remember that dynamics are important and that amps are 90% of tone. In other words, have good gear. Oh, and get a les paul. We both know its time. Remember THERE IS STILL TIME

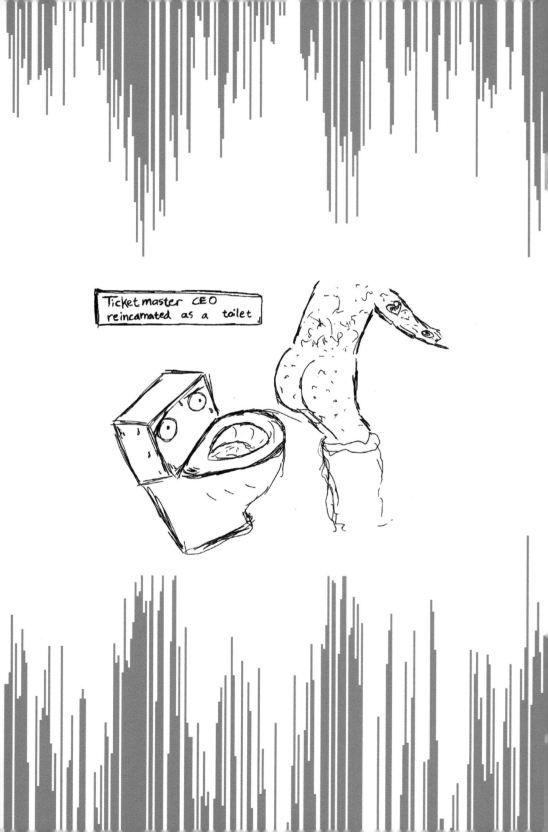

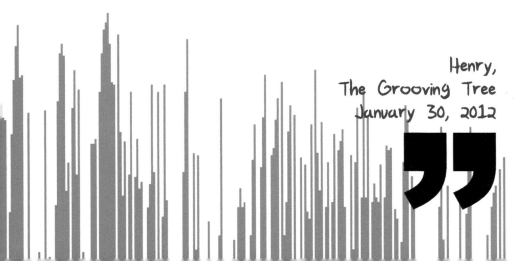

Good afternoon, Madison, the time is officially 12:04. You're listening to WSUM 91.7 FM Madison.

Now, my name is Henry, I'll be taking over for the next hour or so.

You'll notice I'm a little out of breath. I ran up here as fast as I could.

Missed the noon mark but we'll have some good jams coming your way...

regardless of how late I am.

Henry,
The Grooving Tree
January 30, 2012

THE MIS-ADVENTURES OF BURCHARD AND HAWKINS: A TRILOGY

By Henry Mackaman

THE
DEADLY
OSTRICH

Art by Danielle D'Silva.

1: THE DEADLY OSTRICH

"A writer may tell me that he thinks man will ultimately become an ostrich. I cannot properly contradict him."
-Thomas Malthus

This morning I received a call from the chief of police proclaiming the death of Gregory Engle, my grandfather, who had apparently been killed by complications resulting from a confrontation with an escaped zoo ostrich, accompanied by a severe allergic reaction induced by peanut butter. The police were confounded as to how the rogue ostrich escaped and made the half-mile journey to my grandfather's home, and where the large quantity of peanut butter came from. Thus, many questions were left unanswered. Although I hadn't spoken to my grandfather in years, the news of his death was unsettling. I immediately sat down, not from overwhelming grief, but rather because I had suffered a leg cramp while playing tennis with Jerome. As I pondered the benefits of stretching and cost-conscious coffins, the phone rang.

"Burchard? Is that you? It is I, Gail, your sister."

"Yes, good afternoon, dear sister. For what do I owe this pleasure?"

"Cut the crap, Burchard, you know very well why I'm calling, and I would like to make it very clear that you won't see a cent of that money. That is all. Good-bye, Burchard."

The harsh click of Gail hanging up stung my ear, and I grimaced, not because of the coldness of my sister's tone, but because the leg cramp I sustained whilst playing tennis with Jerome was flaring up. What money was Gail talking about? I certainly didn't need any more of it, considering my last novel sold quite well. Gail herself shouldn't be too concerned with money; in fact, she should've stopped being concerned with it the moment she said "I do" to Willis Monroe, multi-millionaire and investment guru. As I pondered the benefits of good investments and simple, yet elegant, funeral flower arrangements, the phone rang once more.

"Burchard, it is I, Willis Monroe, multi-millionaire and investment guru."

"Ah, hello, Willis. How has life been treating you?"

"Cut the crap, kid, we both know what's at stake here. I'll put fifty grand on the table right now, you just say the word," said Willis urgently.

"Willis, old boy, I honestly haven't a clue what you are referencing! It seems that there has been a mis . . . ,"

"All right, smart guy, 100k, take it or leave it. That's my final offer. You come highly recommended, and I am completely serious here." Willis began to sound desperate, his voice shaking as he spoke. "Look, I know what I'm getting into."

"Willis? Willis Monroe?" I questioned with an arched eyebrow.

"Yes, I'm Willis Monroe, and you're Burchard English, the one and only 'Deadly Ostrich.'"

"Oh, Willis, old boy, you are speaking to Burchard Engle, the brother of your wife, Gail!" I said with a chuckle.

"Oh, Burchard, hello! I'm sorry, dear boy, I intended to ring Burchard English, but it appears as if I've dialed the wrong number!" explained the millionaire.

"Don't think of it, old boy!" I chuckled.

"What?" shouted Willis into the receiver.

"I said, don't think of it!" I repeated gingerly.

"What did you say? I'm afraid I'm a bit hard of hearing!" Willis replied, continuing to shout.

"I said . . ."

The click of Willis hanging up was startling, and I dropped the phone on the floor.

What was that about? Who was this so-called "Deadly Ostrich," and did he have anything to do with my grandfather's death? Was this related to the money Gail mentioned earlier? How does one make salmon-flavored cream cheese? As these questions raced through my mind, Mr. Ashworth, my butler, entered the sitting room.

"Good afternoon, Mr. Engle," exclaimed the ancient butler in his monotone voice. Apart from his bushy eyebrows, Mr. Ashworth's gray goatee was the only hair on his wrinkled head, and it moved ever so gently as he spoke. His shoulders hunched over a great deal, and it appeared that he had no neck. I've always thought of him as a turtle who'd lost its shell.

"Pardon my observation, Mr. Engle, but you look quite constipated," noted the butler.

"Mr. Ashworth, I'm afraid I'm being pained internally by most foul circumstances."

"I'll get the laxatives," replied the butler as he turned to leave the room.

"No, no, foul thoughts, Mr. Ashworth, and quite foul thoughts indeed. Nevertheless, retrieve the laxatives. I've invited Hawkins over for tea, and he's twenty minutes late. I'd like to teach him a lesson."

"Hmm, I've always thought Mr. Hawkins was quite regular . . . ," explained the surprised butler as he turned to leave the room.

Perhaps Hawkins will have some good insight on the mystery surrounding my grandfather's death. He is an accountant, after all, and nothing gets past an accountant.

Mr. Ashworth returned with the unlabeled powder laxatives just as a knock was heard at the door. Mr. Ashworth went to answer it, but just as his hand extended towards the doorknob, the large oak door swung open violently, revealing a smiling Hawkins Worthington. The alarmed butler disappeared into a heap behind the door as Hawkins made his way toward "Hello, Burchard! How are you on this fine afternoon?"

chuckled the grinning accountant. He stopped in his tracks and stared at me. "Pardon my asking, but are you constipated?" A groan escaped from behind the door. "My, no wonder you look so down, your stomach sounds awful!" Hawkins proceeded to sit down in the armchair across from the coffee table, and he crossed his lanky legs, revealing hideous puke-green argyle socks.

Accountants are not known for their fashion sense.

"Never mind that, Hawkins, my grandfather was found dead this morning, and it appears to be fowl play."

"Foul play? You mean murder?" gasped Hawkins.

"No, I mean fowl play—it appears that grandfather was killed by an ostrich."

"Are ostriches considered to be fowls? I always thought they belonged to the ratite order Struthioniformes group . . ." Hawkins and I locked eyes as silence ensued.

"Nevertheless, my grandfather is dead and I want answers," I said with a hint of frustration. "And to top it off, I received a phone call from Willis Monroe who mistook me for a man he called 'The Deadly Ostrich,' whom he wanted to pay one hundred thousand dollars. I don't understand it, Hawkins, I just don't understand it . . ." I rose from my chair and stroked my chin. "And before that, my sister called and informed me that I 'wouldn't see a cent of that money . . .'"

"You really ought to work on your thinking face," muttered Hawkins.

"Whatever do you mean?" I asked defensively.

"Well, in the context of murderous ostriches it's clear that your face indicates analytical thought, but to the untrained eye you simply appear constipated."

"Never mind my thinking face, Hawkins! Focus!" I said with a blush.

"Ah, yes, ahem. Do you think Willis and Gail have anything to do with your grandfather's death?" asked the inquisitive accountant.

"Perhaps this is something best discussed over tea," I replied. "Mr. Ashworth! Would you be so kind as to fetch us some tea?" A groan echoed throughout the sitting room. "Mr. Ashworth, a good man and a good butler, but always sleeping on the job."

"On another note, it appears as if your house is haunted," noted the wide-eyed Hawkins. "I know a priest who can rid your house of spirits for cheap. He's a little old and a little senile, but he really pushes the envelope in the field of spirit-ridding."

"Nonsense, Hawkins, you really ought to keep your wits about you." A ghostly cackle resonated throughout the room. "If you could leave the priest's number on the coffee table, I'll give him a call as soon as I can." Silence ensued as Hawkins and I nervously surveyed the room for potential poltergeists. "This is all beside the point, Hawkins, we must get to the bottom of this," I sternly proclaimed.

Hawkins's forehead curled up in thought. "Hawkins, your thinking face looks as if you've just smelled a used diaper," I noted with a smirk.

"First off, you are immature, and you appear constipated. Secondly, we really ought to find this 'Deadly Ostrich' fellow. Do you have any idea who he might be?"

"Well as a matter of fact, Willis mentioned his name, and it happens to be very similar to mine. If only I could remember it . . ." I curled up my forehead like Hawkins in an attempt to jog my memory.

Mr. Ashworth had now mostly recovered from his confrontation with the door and limped into the sitting room with the tea.

"Well this just doesn't make sense . . ." stated the butler, making his presence known.

"We are well aware, Mr. Ashworth—my grandfather's death is quite the mystery," I proclaimed.

"No, no, I'm not talking about that, I'm simply observing that although Mr. Worthington's face looks as if he's smelled fecal matter, Mr. Engle looks as if he hasn't moved his bowels in a decade."

"Mr. Ashworth, that is really very irrelevant and inappropriate. I will not have you sink to childish potty humor to get a cheap laugh—every writer would agree."

"Yes, Mr. Engle . . . ," muttered the disheartened butler as he set down the tea.

"Would you like sugar with your tea?" I asked Hawkins with a sly smile.

"No thank you, Burchard, that is quite all right," replied Hawkins gingerly.

"Have it your way," I shrugged as I poured the unlabeled powder laxatives into the tea.

"Oh, Burchard, I said no sugar!" protested the accountant as the phone rang.

Mr. Ashworth picked up the receiver and casually put it to his ear. The butler's face didn't move a muscle as the sounds of the agitated caller rambled on. "It's for you," stated the butler as he extended the phone toward me. "I believe it is your sister, Gail."

Hawkins and I shared a concerned look as I took the phone. Hawkins nudged over closer so he could hear, all the while sipping his tea.

"Burchard, we have much to discuss. Our plan is due to be carried out this evening, and I need to know that everything will go accordingly." It was Gail all right, presumably repeating her husband's mistake and again dialing the wrong number.

"Wait!" whispered Hawkins. "Play along with it! This may lead us right to this 'Deadly Ostrich' fellow!" I nodded in approval.

"Ahem, yes, our plans . . . ," I replied in a deep and (hopefully) convincing tone.

"Burchard, is something wrong?" countered Gail suspiciously.

"Uh, yes, as a matter of fact I did come down with a mild cold this morning . . ."

"Well pardon me if I'm wrong, but you sound a bit constipated," said Gail rather matter-of-factly.

"She's right, you know . . . ," whispered Hawkins with a smile.

"Is there someone with you?" responded Gail with an ever-increasingly suspicious tone.

"Um no, no . . . ," I chuckled deeply, "that was just the wind . . ."

"Never mind the wind, we have business to attend to. As you know, after you kill my husband, there will be bags of money with your name on them. After all, you come highly recommended. Now listen, I want to know how you plan to kill him. The Ostrich was genius in getting rid of that old-timer, and after I get the inheritance, there will be enough for you, Mr. English, to retire."

As I swiftly hung up the phone, presumably causing Gail to grimace as a result of the overpowering click of rejection, a grin sprang to my lips. Hawkins sat wide-eyed with his mouth gaping.

"Quick, Hawkins, retrieve the public directory!" I shouted with a sudden burst of energy. Hawkins leapt from his seat and quickly returned from the pantry with the directory. I hastily flipped to the "E" section and scanned the page for "English." And there it was: "Burchard English," right beneath my own name, "Burchard Engle."

"Aha, Hawkins, that explains the mixed-up calls! Mr. English is the name right below mine! Hmm, Gail is sure to realize her mistake soon, as she just dialed me not five minutes before you knocked on the door. If only we had Burchard English's address, then we could get to him before Gail does . . ." I stroked my chin in thought.

"Well isn't Mr. English's address listed in the directory?" questioned Hawkins. I looked down at the page. Sure enough, it was right there!

"Sure enough, it is right here!" I gasped. "Quick, get my coat, Mr. Ashworth, I have a mystery to solve!"

"Are you sure we're qualified to solve a mystery, Burchard? I mean, you're a novelist, and I'm an accountant!" protested my hesitant and unfashionable friend.

"Nonsense, Hawkins, we may not be detectives, but we are a team, and besides, now that I think about it, there is little-to-no mystery involved. We already know my greedy sister Gail is behind it all."

"Well then, why are we going to confront this Deadly Ostrich fellow?" replied Hawkins.

"Well frankly, I am quite bored."

"Yes, me too." Hawkins shrugged.

"Mr. Engle, I am quite bored as well," contributed the butler in his trademark monotone voice.

"Very well, Mr. Ashworth, let us all track down the 'Deadly Ostrich'!" I shouted as my group of unlikely detectives departed the flat.

As my group of unlikely detectives approached the flat of the Deadly Ostrich, which looked uncannily like my own, Hawkins had some doubts.

"I have some doubts," said Hawkins sheepishly.

"Nonsense, Hawkins, give the door a good knocking!" I said as I took a step back from the large oak door. The sound of Hawkins's knock rang loud and true, but there was no immediate response.

"Just open the door, dear boy. It's what you're good at . . . ," contributed the sarcastic butler. Hawkins proceeded to fling the door open violently, resulting in a slight thud and several soft moans heard from behind the door.

"I don't like it, Burchard. It seems like this flat is haunted too!" noted the nervous accountant.

"Nonsense!" shouted a mysterious voice from inside the flat. The voice's body made its way to the door. Mr. English's messy brown hair and sunken eyes looked remarkably like my own, and he wore the exact same shoes.

"It seems we are wearing the exact same shoes!" said Mr. English as a smile broke out across his face.

"That is a very odd first observation to make about a man whom you have just met," I declared.

"Not nearly as odd as a troupe of strangers barging into my apartment unannounced!" countered the equally witty Burchard.

"Well that isn't nearly as odd as an assassin whose weapon of choice is an ostrich," I replied with a cold smirk.

"Ah, it appears you know more about me than I know about you . . . perhaps this is something best discussed over tea," Mr. English said as he walked back toward the sitting room.

"Mr. Dustin! Would you be so kind as to fetch us some tea?" A groan echoed throughout the sitting room. We all stopped a moment to survey the room for potential poltergeists.

"Mr. Dustin, a good man and a good butler, but always sleeping on the job," resolved the slightly embarrassed assassin. "How about we take a little walk to the café down the street? I always say that the most personal matters should be discussed in public. What say you, gentlemen?"

"I think I'll stay behind," replied Mr. Ashworth. "I am quite sleepy."

"Very well Mr. Ashworth, but Hawkins and I have very pressing issues to discuss," I said, forgetting that the flat I was currently in was not actually my own. The other Burchard arched an eyebrow at my unintentional gaffe.

"Very well, let us go to the café!" exclaimed the Deadly Ostrich.

The café down the street was a small rundown joint simply christened Shady Business. The plaster walls were in disrepair, and weeds protruded through cracks in the aging patio. The peeling red paint from the chairs flaked onto my waistcoat, and everyone in the group seemed a little uneasy with the condition of the establishment. Besides exchanging names, not a word had been spoken since we left the flat. Suddenly, the silence was broken by Hawkins.

"Bathroom!" shouted the blushing accountant with a sense of urgency, as he leapt from his chair and briskly waddled toward decrepit sign reading "Rstroo."

"What's gotten into him?" questioned my counterpart.

"More like what's gotten out of him!" I chuckled.

"Oh please do not sink to childish potty humor to get a cheap laugh—every writer would agree," countered the stone-faced and fashionable man.

"You're a writer?" I questioned with a smile.

"Indeed I am, and a damn good one at that!" he replied.

"I, too, am a novelist!" Mr. English gave a look of approval. "Hold on a minute, I thought you were an assassin!" I whispered urgently.

"No sir, I am a true novelist! That whole assassin business is merely a hobby."

"Hobby?" I questioned with an arched eyebrow.

"Well to be honest, being a novelist is quite boring. I needed to find something to excite my senses, something to fill my lungs with joy! At first I tried playing the saxophone . . ."

"The saxophone?" I said with my eyebrow still arched.

"Yes, the saxophone. As it turns out, the saxophone is quite dull as well, so I logically took the next step . . ."

"You became an assassin after dismissing the saxophone?" My eyebrow hurt from all the arching.

"Oh no, dear boy, I took to flying kites!"

"Flying kites?" My eyebrow sank down from pure exhaustion.

"Yes, flying kites. However, there is only so much fun one can have with a sheet of glorified paper tied to a string, so I naturally took to murder."

"Murder?" I gasped.

"Ah, and your hobby must be repeating everything I say," countered Mr. English as an excited Hawkins returned from his adventure.

"Sorry about that," said the relieved and giddy accountant. "I'm not sure what got into me . . ."

"Well, Hawkins, you're just in time to hear Mr. English explain his hobby . . ."

"Never mind that; during my trip to the restroom I made a startling discovery! This café is no café—it's a brothel! There are secret rooms in the back!" shouted the excited Hawkins, which attracted the attention of a very large man wearing lipstick who appeared to be the owner of Shady Business.

"Great. Look what you've done!" I whispered to

Hawkins as the underdressed man approached the table. The basket of fruit precariously balanced on his head matched his skimpy vibrant underwear, the only article of clothing on his bottom half. His arms were almost as thick and hairy as his black beard, but it was his large breasts that attracted the majority of my attention.

"May I help you, gentlemen? It is quite a hot day, perhaps I can interest you in some sex?" offered the strange gentlemen seductively.

"Let me get this straight—the name of this café is Shady Business, which is actually a front for a brothel, and you just waltz right up to us and ask us if we want sex?" questioned Hawkins as he tried to arch an eyebrow, but only ended up squinting.

"First off, the name Shady Business keeps the cops oblivious, and secondly, I overheard your realization just a moment ago." The transvestite then looked over at me. "And you remind me of someone I know, someone cute . . . ," finished the man with a wry smile.

Mr. English leaned in toward Hawkins and me. "I'm sorry, boys, I've never been here before . . ." He then leaned back in the rickety chair and turned toward the prostitute. "Do you serve any actual refreshments at this establishment?"

"We do serve a dessert item. It's called a banana twist, named after myself . . . ," replied Banana Twist seductively.

"We'll have three of those please," replied the uncomfortable part-time assassin. Banana Twist winked at him before returning inside the unconvincing café.

"Well that was odd . . . ," Mr. English said, chuckling.

"Not as odd as an assassin whose weapon of choice is an ostrich." I quickly countered.

"First of all, for a writer you're very unoriginal. Secondly, I am not really an assassin, per se. I only create fatal situations," said Burchard quite frankly.

"You create fatal situations?" I asked with an arched eyebrow.

"There you go again, repeating everything I say! Also might I add that you look constipated when you arch your eyebrow. No, I am not a murderer. Yes, I create fatal situations, and it just so happens that all of those fatal situations involve ostriches. You might be wondering, 'Why ostriches?'" I opened my mouth to speak but the other Burchard glared at me. Hawkins continued to act like a nervous statue. The assassin took a deep breath and continued.

"While on a trip to the zoo in my youth, I brought with me a peanut butter sandwich. I became overpowered by hunger while standing next to the ostrich enclosure and began eating it."

"Where is this story going?" asked the worst-dressed man at the table. Mr. English gave him a menacing glare.

"As I bit into the sandwich, I noticed that the ostrich in the cage had advanced toward me. He looked hungrier than I, so dismissing the zoo placards, I threw the sandwich into the enclosure. That ostrich went wild. The peanut butter changed him; he became crazed, uncontrollable, murderous . . . Watching that ostrich instilled a fire within me, a fire that burns to this day . . ." The novelist looked philosophically out into the distance.

"So you're telling me that you create 'fatal situations' by leaving a trail of peanut butter straight to the victim, and then you simply release a hungry ostrich?" asked the accountant.

"Heavens no!" chuckled Mr. English. "The ostrich doesn't have to be hungry! All the other aspects of your theory are indeed correct though. However, it is getting harder and harder to free the ostriches, because the zookeepers install more advanced security systems after every escapade."

"So that's how you killed my grandfather, Gregory Engle, and how you plan to kill Willis Monroe, multi-millionaire and investment guru?" I asked in amazement. Mr. English went pale.

"Gregory Engle was your son?" gasped the assassin.

"No, I said he was my grandfather."

"Gregory Engle was your grandfather?" gasped the assassin.

"Yes, he was, and now he is dead because of you!"

I shouted as I stood up from the table and pointed a trembling finger at the culprit.

"Then you must be Burchard Engle . . . ," muttered Mr. English.

"Yes, he is!" shouted Hawkins as he stood up and pointed a trembling finger at me.

"Hawkins, that is quite all right . . . ," I muttered, and the embarrassed accountant sat down.

"I'm afraid I'm being pained internally by the most foul circumstances . . . ," whispered Mr. English with a shaking voice.

"Would you like some laxatives?" I asked while reaching into my pocket. Hawkins gave me a suspicious look.

"No, no, foul thoughts, and quite foul thoughts indeed . . . You see, Mr. Engle, you're on my hit list . . . ," replied Mr. English as he produced a small black notebook from his jacket. He flipped through it urgently, before grimly pausing on a page. "Yes, right here . . . ," said the assassin as he showed me the page and gestured toward my name. Sure enough, it was right there.

"Sure enough, it is right here!" I exclaimed, transfixed on the scribbled ink. It was then that I noticed my sister Gail's name below mine. "My sister Gail's name is on that list . . . ," I noted as I sat down, not from the shock that someone wanted my sister and me dead, but because the leg cramp I had suffered while playing tennis with Jerome was acting up again.

"No one will harm my dear sister!" I shouted at the assassin.

"But, Burchard, she was the one who hired me to kill you . . ."

"The bitch must die!" I yelled. "But why would she want me dead?"

"She wants Gregory Engle's fortune all to herself! How did you not put that together?" shouted the assassin in amazement.

"Ah, perhaps there was a little mystery involved after all!" said the smiling accountant.

"Hmm, I suppose all the elderly have fortunes these days," I said. "But that still leaves the matter of whether or not Mr. English will do to me what Gail Monroe hired him to do to Gregory . . ." It was then that I realized Banana Twist had been standing behind us with the plate of frozen chocolate-covered bananas.

"Here are your banana twists . . . ," muttered the obviously upset Banana Twist, who then proceeded to stare at us sadly before briskly returning inside the café.

"Well I certainly can't kill anyone who I enjoy a banana twist with!" chuckled Mr. English as he took a bite of the frozen banana. "This is delicious!"

"Well that certainly is good, but I still have some questions for you," I proclaimed.

"How much do you think Banana Twist heard?" questioned the unfashionable accountant.

"Never mind that, Hawkins! Now, Mr. English, what contact have you had with Willis Monroe, multi-millionaire and investment guru?"

"Willis hired me to kill his wife, Gail," replied Mr. English grimly.

"Oh yes, that's why her name was on the list. Well, all right then."

"You don't want to know why?" asked the assassin.

"Well I suppose, I mean, if you want to tell me . . . ," I replied.

"You see, Burchard, we're solving a mystery we didn't know existed!" exclaimed Hawkins excitedly.

"Well, Willis found out that Gail planned to have him killed, so he planned to have her killed. Oh yes, did I mention that Gail planned to have Willis killed? She wants his money too."

"Let me get this straight, Gail hired you to kill Willis, my grandfather, and myself for our money, and Willis hired you to kill Gail after finding out about it?"

"I come highly recommended," replied the calm part-time assassin.

"Wait, but how would Willis pay you if you killed him for Gail first?" asked Hawkins.

"Weren't you listening, Hawkins? Mr. English doesn't kill for money—he kills for the thrill!" I shouted.

"No, Hawkins has a good point, and to be quite honest I didn't really think that through . . . ," exclaimed the pondering assassin as he stroked his chin and arched an eyebrow.

"The thrill is nice, but you can't buy banana twists with thrills," said Mr. English before biting into the frozen banana.

"Perhaps you should have them both pay a down payment and then skip town!" said Hawkins excitedly.

"That is a grand idea!" exclaimed Mr. English as he stood up. "But frankly, I would like to kill someone . . ."

"Why not kill Gail?" I said. "She probably deserves it most."

"Well, what's in it for me?" responded Mr. English slyly.

"But Willis already hired you to kill her!" I protested. The assassin looked unimpressed. "You'll receive a great thrill . . ." The assassin remained frowning. "And fifteen banana twists!" I offered.

"Done!" exclaimed the excited assassin as he grabbed his coat and turned to go.

"But, Mr. English, when will you do this dirty deed?" I questioned.

"What better day for a murder than a funeral?" The assassin smiled.

My grandfather's funeral was held in a moderately respectable church not three blocks from my flat. Although the service was held in a small room, it was not nearly full. The aged attendees awkwardly gazed about like an assortment of confused animals lost in the city, and they looked about as thrilled as a patient just prior to the doctor saying "Cough," but then again they did not seem to be especially exciting people in the first place. My grandfather was not a terribly interesting man, and he had made friends who appeared to have the collective wit of a tub of salmon-flavored cream cheese. In fact, being murdered by an ostrich consumed by a peanut-butter-induced craze was probably the most interesting thing ever to happen to Gregory Engle.

I spotted Willis and Gail sitting in the front row,

Willis appearing bored, and Gail appearing sad. Say what you will about her morality, but Gail always had a knack for acting. I thought it might be fun to engage them in idle conversation with the knowledge of Mr. English's little black notebook. I tried to persuade Hawkins, who had arrived twenty minutes early, to join me in conversation with the murderous couple, but the accountant found this idea too stressful and stayed behind, seated in the pew. Thus Hawkins, who had attended the funeral out of sheer boredom, found himself not only bored out of his mind, but also in a very uncomfortable and dusty black suit sitting alone in a church.

"Hello, Gail."

"Hello, Burchard. I see you're still alive and well," replied my sister coldly.

"I see you two decided to ostracize yourselves from the rest of the group," I countered.

"We are just so glad to have each other . . . ," replied the investment guru, who, despite his best efforts, could not act to save his life.

"Plus, when you sit in the front row you don't have to worry about getting people out of the way . . . ," I casually said.

Hawkins, who had momentarily contemplated taking a nap, decided instead to join the conversation. "Hello, Willis and Gail, pleasure to see you," exclaimed Hawkins politely. Gail gave the accountant a glare that could freeze a campfire.

"Burchard, it would be wise to find yourself a seat. The grief is overwhelming poor Willis, and conversation is much too stressful on him in this trying hour."

"Willis and Grandfather were not even related, and, in fact, I'm quite certain they never spoke a word!" I protested.

"Burchard, although you are rude and ungrateful, I must say that there is something pleasantly different about you . . . ," observed my evil sister.

"Well, during a recent trip to the doctor, it was discovered that I had been battling severe constipation, but now I'm cured."

"I always thought you were quite regular," said

the surprised Hawkins. The rest of the group gave the accountant a bewildered look.

"I'm glad to hear you finally cut the crap, kid!" Willis chuckled.

"Willis, please do not sink to childish potty humor to get a cheap laugh—every writer would agree," commented Gail.

"But you're not a writer!" I protested.

"No, but if I were, I wouldn't endorse such immature comments. Besides, I've read your books, Burchard, you really ought to take my advice," commented Gail smugly. Before I could retaliate, an aging man in a black robe appeared at the podium.

"We are gathered here today to join Crawford and Grace in holy matrimony . . . ," began the senile priest before an altar boy rushed up to the podium and whispered the reality of the situation into his wrinkled ear.

"We are gathered here today to celebrate the life of Gregory Engle, a great man, who was killed by one of God's strangest creatures."

"This is the old spirit-ridding priest I was telling you about!" whispered Hawkins excitedly.

"Ah yes, the one who 'pushes the envelope in the business of spirit ridding,'" I whispered sarcastically. The disheartened Hawkins looked down with a frown.

"If anybody has anything to say about Gregory's life, now is the time to do so. Afterwards, we will go over Mr. Engle's last will and testament." The old priest slowly shuffled from the podium in a coughing fit toward the bathroom. There was a short pause before an old woman from the back began to make her way to the podium. However, she was quickly cut off by Gail.

"I think I speak for us all when I say that Gregory's memory is best remembered in silence, so all of us can truly and individually appreciate his vibrant life!" Gail's acting abilities were fading with greed, and her plastered smile was accompanied by glaring eyes, as if to dare any potential speaker to rise. The old woman from the back immediately returned to her seat.

"Now, I think it wise to deal with the dreadful

matter of the will quickly, so as to get it out of the way, and seeing as it deals with just Burchard and myself, the rest of you who don't have anything to do with it can leave," Gail stated coldly.

"But I was told there were to be bagels and salmon-flavored cream cheese . . . ," protested an old man in the back.

"Why don't you take your bagel and shove it up your . . . ," Gail surveyed the crowd and saw a collective expression of terror. "I mean, why don't you take a trip to the bagel shop down the street . . ."

The disheartened old man looked down with a frown and turned toward the church door. The rest of the crowd followed suit, leaving only Hawkins, Willis, Gail, myself, and a man who appeared to be a lawyer (they all look the same). The priest appeared from the bathroom holding an envelope, presumably containing the last will and testament of Gregory Engle.

"Hawkins, perhaps you should wait for me outside . . . ," I muttered. Hawkins nodded and quickly exited the church. The old priest walked up to the podium with the envelope and attempted to open it. But freeing the will from the confines of the envelope proved too difficult a task for the old and senile priest, who then proceeded to drop it on the podium. To make matters worse, the old priest physically could not push the envelope to the top of the podium, and, on cue, an altar boy swiftly rushed to his aid, opening the stubborn envelope.

"Ahem . . . ," he began, "I will now read the last will and testament of Gregory Engle . . ." Gail fidgeted nervously in her chair. "I, Gregory Engle, son of James and Clarice Engle, leave my fortune to be split evenly between my two loving grandchildren, Gail and Burchard." The priest proceeded to dig his hand into the envelope, producing two checks. Gail jumped out of her seat and snatched one from the old man's hand, startling him and causing him to fall over. Gail looked at the paper in disbelief.

"8 dollars and 33 cents? 8 dollars and 33 cents?!" shouted Gail. She rushed down and grabbed the silent lawyer by the collar. "Were you his lawyer?" screamed Gail.

"How could you tell?" exclaimed the surprised lawyer.

"You all look the same," noted Willis quietly.

"What happened to the fortune!" my sister shouted, not letting go of the lawyer's collar.

"Well, it just so happens that I have his financial records right here," explained the lawyer as he produced a briefcase filled with official-looking documents. He flipped through several documents before pausing on one particular page. The lawyer looked puzzled.

"Well it seems that Mr. Engle made several large purchases before he died . . . ," said the confused lawyer.

"What purchases? Where were they made?" shouted the angry female inheritor.

"Well it appears that Mr. Engle spent the vast majority of his fortune at an establishment called Shady Business . . . ," finished the lawyer. My jaw dropped.

"Shady Business? What the hell is Shady Business? As his inheritor, I demand to acquire the goods he purchased from this so-called Shady Business!" continued Gail on the verge of breaking down.

"I'm not sure you want what Shady Business is selling!" I chuckled in delight. Just then the door to the church burst open. Two police officers escorted a handcuffed Burchard English down the aisle.

"What's going on here?" screamed Gail.

"We caught this fellow on the lamb . . . ," explained the first officer.

"You mean he was running away?" I questioned.

"No, I mean we caught him riding a lamb toward the church. He was leading an assortment of animals through the city," explained the second officer. "We believe he helped them escape from the local zoo . . ."

"However," began the first officer, "Mr. English has agreed to give us information on a murder conspiracy in exchange for his freedom."

"However, we need to know that his information is true before we can let him go. He said that a 'Burchard Engle' would back him up," finished the second officer.

"I can indeed! Arrest Willis and Gail Monroe!" I said, smiling as I stood up and pointed a finger at an enraged Gail.

"Good enough for me!" said the officers in unison as they released the novelist/assassin, and advanced toward the estranged couple.

The funeral attendees, who had all recently purchased bagels, saw the assortment of seemingly lost animals outside the church and decided to investigate. One of the bagel-wielding attendees wore all black like the rest, but only sported a miniscule pair of black underwear on his bottom half. He and the rest of the attendees returned just in time to see the handcuffed couple escorted from the church.

"I thought you only used ostriches?" I asked the recently freed assassin.

"I normally do, but the zookeepers outfitted the ostrich enclosure with motion censors and an intricate series of padlocks. I, seeing as all the zoo's security budget had been spent on the ostrich enclosure, released all the other animals with relatively little difficulty. Also, I believe you forgot your butler, Mr. Ashworth, at my flat the other day. He appears to think my flat is your own, and thus refuses to leave," explained Mr. English as Hawkins urgently approached us.

"There is someone here who wants to see you!" exclaimed the winded accountant.

"Whomever do you mean . . ." I asked before catching a glimpse of the advancing transvestite.

"Hello, Burchard," said Banana Twist seductively.

"Banana! I hear you've received the majority of Gregory's fortune! I only got eight dollars," I said, producing the wimpy check from my jacket pocket.

"Ah, just enough to cover the banana twists you and your friends forgot to pay for the other day," countered Banana Twist as he snatched the check from my hand. "Indeed, it is true that I received most of the fortune, but it was never about the money. I loved Gregory Engle, and he loved me. When I heard he was gone, I didn't think I could keep on living. At first I thought it was just fowl play . . ."

"So you knew he was murdered all along?" I questioned.

"No, I knew he was killed by an ostrich, but then

I discovered it was really foul play when I overheard you and your friends at the café . . ."

"First of all, ostriches are a part of the ratite order Struthioniformes group. Secondly, what are you going to do with all that money?" asked the intruding Hawkins.

"Well, let's keep this quiet, but I'm getting revenge. I've hired an assassin to kill Gail Monroe . . . ," answered the café-owning transvestite.

"An assassin?" asked Hawkins and I in unison.

"He comes highly recommended . . . ," continued Banana Twist. I looked around for Mr. English, but he was nowhere to be found. Banana Twist motioned for Hawkins and I to come closer.

"They call him, The Deadly Ostrich . . . "

||

Wisconsin Union Directorate Performing Arts Committee Presents

21ˢᵗ Annual Marcia Légère PLAY FESTIVAL

March 10 at 7pm & March 11 at 3pm

Memorial Union Fredric March Play Circle

Marcia Légère-Binns in 1945

"The Deadly Ostrich" *won the Marcia Legere Play Festival contest & was performed Spring 2012 at the University of Wisconsin-Madison.*

2: THE GOLDEN-BEAKED RAINBOW FINCH

Although the letter arrived this morning, the thought of it stayed with me well into the afternoon. I couldn't seem to shake the image of the blood-red wax seal, formally caging the crisp yellowed page, plagued by ink as black as the depths of a lawyer's soul. What could be done about it? How was I to escape from the letter's horrifying proposition? I decided to call my lowly butler, Mr. Ashworth, into the sitting room to discuss the predicament.

The aging butler hobbled into the sitting room upon hearing his name, dressed in the same stale-smelling gray suit he had worn since my childhood. Why do people of a certain age smell so foul?

"Mr. Engle, I am glad you called for me. I have been meaning to ask you about something," croaked the decaying butler.

"Yes, anything for you, Mr. Ashworth," I responded gingerly.

"I would like a raise."

"A raise? Heavens no! Do you think I am made of bank notes? Besides, what do you need money for?"

"Well, for one thing, I lack the funds for any new

clothes. This is the only suit I own, and I cannot wash what I must wear."

"Nonsense, Mr. Ashworth; if anything, you should invest in some soap. That way, you won't smell like a barrel monkey. Besides, there are more important issues at hand, namely this letter which I hold in my hand." My wrinkled servant squinted silently at the parchment.

"Ah yes, *that* letter. Shall I prepare your travel case?"

"Mr. Ashworth, although your odor is comparable to a steaming heap of elephant dung, you read me like a children's book!" I exclaimed joyously.

"I cannot read, sir . . . ," replied the butler in his trademark monotone rasp.

It was at that moment when a series of overly confident knocks inflicted the door with what must've been a considerable amount of pain. Mr. Ashworth waddled over to the beaten door with much difficulty, and, just as he extended a hand toward the knob, the large slab of oak swung open violently, revealing my smiling loyal friend and accountant, Hawkins. The butler disappeared without a sigh behind the door as Hawkins proceeded to enter the sitting room.

Hawkins's unruly dirty blond bangs disregarded the part on the left side of his scalp and cascaded over his eyes (although I find Hawkins's coiffure obnoxious, his long locks are without question his defining feature). For someone in such dire need of a haircut, Hawkins seemed oddly happy. So happy, in fact, that his smile leveled my frown, and together we made a very indifferent expression, much like that of a man just told his lawyer has been brutally beaten to death with a horseshoe.

"Good day, Hawkins," I groaned.

"Why the long face?" responded the cheerful accountant. "More legal troubles?"

"No, not this time. I am dealing with something far worse . . ." I looked pensively off into the corner of the room.

"Even worse than the time your grandfather's fortune was given to that transvestite café owner instead of you?" The shaggy-haired accountant smirked.

"The money was rightfully hers, I mean his, I mean, I had nothing to contest!"

"But then you hired that lawyer to sue the transvestite, resulting in both public humiliation and substantial legal fees, correct?"

"That was a misunderstanding . . . ," I stuttered.

"And then you were caught in the dead of night outside your lawyer's house wearing a ski mask, holding a horseshoe . . ."

"They didn't prove anything!" I bellowed, my face growing as red as a baboon's bottom. "Where is Mr. Ashworth? Why is he always disappearing?" Hawkins rolled his eyes at the change of subject and proceeded to reach for the week-old newspaper resting on the coffee table.

The butler, having gathered enough strength to overcome his most recent conflict with the door, limped silently toward the sofa.

"Good day, Hawkins," offered the butler with all the sarcasm he could muster.

"Same to you, Mr. Ashworth," replied the accountant without looking up from the dated paper.

"You really ought to get a haircut," noted Mr. Ashworth with a frown.

"I've always thought of my long locks as my defining feature." Hawkins shrugged as he brushed his bangs off to the side of his head.

"Never mind your hair, Hawkins, we have much to discuss," I exclaimed as I crossed my legs. Hawkins looked up at me curiously, his hair retreating back across his eyes.

"This morning I received a most distressing letter . . . ," I began sternly. "I'm forbidden from telling you why, but we must go to the Amazon rainforest immediately."

Both the butler and the accountant stared at me in disbelief.

"The Amazon? But why?" protested Hawkins.

"I cannot tell you why!" I retorted. "Mr. Ashworth, arrange for a direct flight to Brazil—all of us are going to the greatest rainforest in the world!" The butler bowed and obediently exited the sitting room.

"You can't expect me to leave my duties in the city to go to Brazil without knowing why!" shouted the now standing Hawkins.

"Fine, Hawkins, I'll tell you why . . ." I looked around the room quickly and saw the painting of a songbird on the mantle. "We will be looking for a bird!"

"What sort of bird?" Hawkins cocked his head in confusion.

"A very elusive bird, some say the most elusive in the world! We will be tracking the . . ." I quickly looked at my golden watch. "The golden-beaked, umm . . ." I then saw the picture of Noah's Ark being encompassed by a rainbow that my mother drew for me when I was a chap.

"The golden-beaked rainbow finch!" I shouted.

"The golden-beaked rainbow finch?" countered Hawkins hesitantly.

"Yes, it is our duty to travel to the Amazon rainforest, then find and kill the elusive golden-beaked rainbow finch!" I exclaimed while jumping to a proud stance.

"Well why didn't you say so? That sounds like great fun!" The excited accountant laughed.

"Well pack your bags, old chap, we have a plane to catch!" I poked my head into the butler's quarters. "Mr. Ashworth, have you purchased our plane tickets?" I heard only silence, and the butler was nowhere in sight. "Where does Mr. Ashworth always disappear to?" I said to no one in particular. A quiet, yet distinguishable, clearing of a throat came from directly behind me, and I jumped at the butler's startlingly close proximity.

"I conveniently purchased the last three remaining tickets for a plane that conveniently departs to Brazil in two hours time," replied the aging butler.

"Goodness, that is quite convenient given the stinginess of the airline industry these days!" I noted with a grin.

"Yes, and bags fly free," added the butler.

"Sweet mother of Zeus! I need to pack!" shouted Hawkins with a smile, and, with a booming slam of the door, he was gone.

"He really ought to be more aggressive with the

door," said the sarcastic butler as he stretched his back.

"You really ought to be more aggressive with the soap," I said as I retreated to the sofa.

The plane greeted the Brazilian runway with a thud, waking me up from a most pleasant dream involving a doomsday machine of my own design and a law school. Hawkins remained asleep on Mr. Ashworth's shoulder, unaware that the butler had been watching him with an unblinking stare for the majority of the trip.

"Mr. Ashworth, please wake up Hawkins," I muttered as I stared out the window.

"How shall I do it, sir?" responded the unblinking butler.

"Anyway you see fit."

I turned around with the ensuing slapping sound to the sight of Hawkins sitting upright with a bright-red crosshatched mark on his cheek. The butler sat exactly where I had last seen him, as if he hadn't moved a muscle. Hawkins turned to me with a look of both horror and confusion. I simply smiled and looked back out the window.

By the time we retrieved our bags from the belly of the plane, Hawkins had forgotten about his rude awakening, although the inexplicable red crosshatched mark presided as his new defining feature. The accountant twitched with excitement as he and Mr. Ashworth lugged my baggage across the airport parking lot.

"When will we get to the rainforest? Are we there yet?" questioned the giddy Hawkins.

"Calm down, Hawkins, we will be there soon!" I chuckled.

"Mr. Engle, I too have a question. How can you possibly afford three round-trip tickets to Brazil, while there is not one cent in your budget for my raise?" protested Mr. Ashworth.

"Because, Mr. Ashworth, my life is at stake," I said with a solemn frown. Mr. Ashworth rolled his eyes as well as my travel case.

"Is that true, Burchard?" questioned the suddenly hesitant accountant.

"As true as my name is Burchard Engle," I responded with the same solemn frown.

"Well then, let's go kill a golden-beaked rainbow finch!" shouted the inspired Hawkins. "I won't let you die, Burchard, I just won't!"

"Right," I muttered as Hawkins wrapped his arms around me with tears in his eyes.

"Also, how do you plan on getting to the rainforest, sir?" questioned Mr. Ashworth.

"Well, to be quite honest, I haven't really thought that through . . ." Hawkins stopped in his tracks and dropped the bags he was carrying. He then sprinted ahead of Mr. Ashworth and me, taking a sharp corner around the block. The butler and I gave each other a look of mutual confusion, when all of a sudden a loud rumbling started up from around the bend. The noise of a throaty motor grew louder, and soon the sight of Hawkins in a weather-beaten Jeep came into view. The old jeep jerked as Hawkins applied the brake, and the sound of the rusty pistons filled the astonished silence held by the butler and myself.

"Stealing a jeep? That's the spirit! What gusto! You are a true friend, Hawkins!" I shouted above the engine's roar as I hurled the bags in the back. I jumped aboard, and although Hawkins and I shared a smile, Mr. Ashworth remained stationary.

"Come on, Mr. Ashworth! Let's get moving!" yelled Hawkins.

"I refuse to be a part of this crime! I'm still under probation after my guilty plea for the accountant massacre of thirty years past!" mouthed the butler, but his words were not strong enough to cross the threshold of sound needed to overpower the engine.

"Get in! Look!" I screamed with a finger pointing to the five angry Brazilian men running at us with machetes. Mr. Ashworth needed no more convincing, and although the butler was quite a few years detached from his youth, he leapt into the jeep with a catlike agility, and Hawkins floored the accelerator. The jeep lurched forward, and Hawkins quickly reached into his coat and produced a pistol.

"Did you get that from the ammunitions bag?" I yelled in confusion.

"No, I always keep a little protection on hand!" chuckled the accountant as he fired a few warning shots at the machete-wielding pursuers.

"You mean to tell me you brought that on the plane?" I shouted in disbelief. Hawkins gave me a sly smile, his hair whipping about wildly in the wind.

"That's the spirit! What gusto!" I chuckled with a grin. I turned around to Mr. Ashworth, who produced a similar pistol from his jacket.

"You too, Mr. Ashworth?" The butler gave a sly grin, and with one shot, one of the presumable jeep owners was on the ground writhing in pain.

"Mr. Ashworth! You've shot someone! What gusto!"

"And you have stated the obvious," replied the unmoved butler, returning the smoking pistol to his jacket pocket. I turned away from the back seat with a slight frown.

"Did you hire Mr. Ashworth without a background check?" asked the concerned Hawkins.

"He's always been in my family!" I protested. "But then again, perhaps those Irish mafia tattoos of his are not as ironic as I once suspected . . ."

Our gang of unlikely thugs drove past the outskirts of town until a thick tangle of trees replaced the cityscape. The easy vibrations from the dated motor numbed my body into a stupor, and waves of drowsiness began to lap against my heavy eyelids. Nevertheless, my mind raced along with the stolen jeep, and yet my thoughts remained focused on one solitary concept: escape.

"I believe we are nearing our destination!" reported the smiling chauffeur.

"I believe you are correct! Pull over in that clearing," I said, pointing a finger toward an opening in the trees. The jeep ground to a halt in a thick cloud of dust, and soon the gear was unloaded and unpacked. After several minutes of picking through the ammunition supply, we had enough bullets to collectively take down an elephant. I looked proudly at my companions as we walked into the trees.

"Well, I'd better load my gun."

Although our expedition hadn't lasted ten minutes, the atmosphere was already filled with tension and distrust. Mr. Ashworth had insisted on burning the jeep to cover up the evidence of our midday escapade, but Hawkins was certain that someone would see the smoke and track us. Conversation between the butler and the accountant ceased immediately. Thus, it was up to me to instigate conversation.

"Has anyone seen that movie? The one with the flying jalopy?" I asked lightheartedly.

"No," came the mutual response from my unintrigued companions.

"How about a map? Have you seen one of those?" snapped Hawkins.

"Dear and naive Hawkins, you forgot that I was born with the great gift of direction. My mum always said there was a pinch of iron in my nose, much like a pigeon, and I always manage to find my way."

"Is that so, Burchard? Well in that case, why don't you kindly point out the entrance to the rainforest?" replied the pessimistic accountant. I looked around for any sign of where we had come in.

"Ah, yes . . . Well, if the North Star is positioned there, and the moss grows on that side of the tree, then I believe we are . . ."

"Lost!" shouted Hawkins. "We are lost, Burchard, and we've only been here for five minutes!"

"To be fair, it has been more like seven minutes," I replied meekly.

"Besides, it doesn't matter if we make it out of this maze alive, because even if we do, we will have no way of making it back to town, because we burned our means of transportation!" Hawkins was turning red with rage.

"And now it won't just be your head in the guillotine, but Mr. Ashworth's and mine as well!"

"First off, the French don't use the guillotine any more; it's passé."

"As a matter of fact, they still do, Burchard. You know why?"

"Because the French are crazy?"

"Well, yes," Hawkins responded with a shrug.

"Secondly, where is Mr. Ashworth?" I said while scanning the surroundings. Hawkins gave a surprised look and surveyed the space to his left, previously occupied by the butler.

"Mr. Ashworth!" I bellowed. The only response was the echo of my voice.

"Where is he always disappearing to?" I asked while putting my hands to my hips, surveying the landscape for a clue of the butler's whereabouts.

"Well, Hawkins, I think we both know what needs to be done," I said solemnly.

"Find Mr. Ashworth as fast as we can so he doesn't die alone in this inhospitable rainforest?"

"No, we must find a place in our hearts for Mr. Ashworth's memory, and then continue on our quest to find the elusive golden-beaked rainb . . ." A gunshot rang out loud and true. I looked over at Hawkins, his gun smoking and his mouth gaping. The accountant stood frozen in the elegant green display of the jungle floor.

"What the . . . ," whispered Hawkins softly, as he began to walk toward his target. The accountant slowly made his way over the natural obstacle course of organic matter in his way.

"Did you just shoot Mr. Ashworth?" I questioned, while slowly pursuing the accountant.

"I'm not sure—I just saw a flash of color and so I shot at it! Perhaps it was the elusive golden-beaked rainbow finch!" shouted Hawkins, his giddy smile returning.

"You saw a flash of color so you shot at it? Good god, man! Also, I doubt that you have killed a golden-beaked rainbow finch." I chuckled.

"And why is that?" questioned the suddenly serious accountant.

"Umm, no reason." I smiled unconvincingly.

"No, Burchard, why do you doubt that I shot the elusive bird?"

"Because . . . umm, well, here it goes . . . I made it up. I made it all up," I replied hesitantly.

"You made what up?" asked the crestfallen Hawkins.

"The golden-beaked rainbow finch, I made it up. It is a fictitious creature—it has not ever been, and never will be, in the realm of existence."

"Made it up? Then why are we in Brazil? What was that letter of yours really about?" shouted the flustered Hawkins.

"The letter was an invitation to my family reunion," I confessed. Hawkins did not move a muscle. He gave me a glare that froze my bones.

"Shit off," muttered Hawkins. "Shit off, you . . . you manipulative geezer!"

"To be fair, you know my family—they are dreadful! All that meaningless small talk and the endless questioning is absolutely horrid."

"You bring me halfway around the world on a wild goose chase, trick me into thinking your life is in danger, and for what? So you can avoid your miserable family? Well, Burchard, you are just as bad as they are! And let's not forget, Mr. Ashworth is probably dead by now because of you!"

"Mr. Ashworth lived a long, meaningful . . . well, a long life, and I knew you'd never come with me to the Amazon if you didn't have a good reason for going! The golden-beaked rainbow finch was only an excuse for adventure!"

"You are unbelievable, Burchard. From here on out, we are done. Don't ever bother to try and talk to me again," said the disheartened Hawkins as he turned and slowly began walking away.

"One last thing, Hawkins, what was it that you shot?" The accountant stopped in his tracks and looked at his feet.

"Burchard, you better come over here . . . "

I traversed the tangle of the trees until I found myself directly by Hawkins's side. There, on the ground, was what could only be described as a golden-beaked rainbow finch.

"Sweet mother of Zeus, a golden-beaked rainbow finch! It is unlike anything I have ever seen!" I gasped in amazement.

"First of all, this bird is mine. Secondly, this doesn't change anything between us. You go one way, and I'll go the other." Hawkins picked up the strange deceased bird.

"Look, Hawkins, like it or not, our chances of survival double if we stay together. I read that in a book," I explained.

"You know what I read in a book? Never trust Burchard!" exclaimed my shaggy-haired companion defiantly.

"That doesn't even make sense," I protested. "Look, let's just stay together, Hawkins, I don't want to be alone . . ." I could sense the compassion in my friend's eyes, but pride got the better of him.

"Fine, we'll stay together, but only so I can use you as a human shield in case we get attacked by elephants." Hawkins's red crosshatched mark was now invisible against his blushing cheeks.

"Elephants? Where do you think we are?"

The hours passed by, but still Hawkins and I remained trapped in the jungle's unforgiving snare. We had no food, and hunger sank its vicious claws into our stomachs. A slight rain drizzled atop our heads, dampening both our clothes and our spirits. The beauty of the jungle was overpowered by our fear that the outside world would forever be lost to our desperate eyes.

"Hawkins, if our situation progresses, and I mean this as a compliment, I feel it would be noble and wise for you to give yourself up to me."

"What?"

"Let me eat you, Hawkins; one of us could survive this terrible ordeal!"

"We've only been lost for five hours!"

"Yes, but who knows when help might come?" I protested while licking my lips.

"Why don't we just eat the golden-beaked rainbow finch?" suggested the accountant. "On second thought, I'll eat the golden-beaked rainbow finch myself. After all, I'm the one who killed it. But for you, Burchard, old friend, I'll let you watch."

"Damn!" I shouted. The accountant pulled the bird from his pack and took a large chomp. I watched in amazement as the once-docile accountant ravaged the bird for its flesh, blood staining his blond bangs. The rainbow feathers fell like leaves, and soon there was little left of the strange bird. Although Hawkins had presumably cured his hunger, something was amiss.

"Hawkins, your eyebrow . . . ," I whispered.

"What about it?" asked the accountant while licking his fingers.

"Why, it seems to be falling off!" I gasped. The bushy blond eyebrow fell onto the Amazonian floor in one clump. The two of us stayed silent as Hawkins's remaining eyebrow followed suit and landed squarely next to the first blond clump. The accountant looked up in horror. It was then that I felt a sharp stinging in my neck.

"Hawkins . . ."

"Yes?"

"Is there a blow-dart in my neck?" I felt my knees buckle with a numbing sensation.

"Yes, Burchard, that looks exactly like a blo . . . " Hawkins then collapsed upon the jungle floor. I lost consciousness and joined the accountant and his eyebrows on the ground.

When I came to, I felt my body crippled with stiffness. My fear of being permanently paralyzed subsided as I slowly realized that my limbs were bound to a stake, but this did not put my mind at ease. Hawkins was conscious and to my left, and although he shared the same fate of being tied to a stake, he was completely hairless and up to his knees in shit.

"Hawkins, you are completely bald and covered in shit!"

"No! My beautiful blonde locks! My defining feature!"

It was then that I noticed our captors. They numbered about fifty, and were of a small stature with weathered, leather-like skin. Their dark eyes fixated upon the strange sight of Hawkins and myself.

"You foreigners have offended Hamer-eek, God of the Sky . . . ," muttered a familiar voice.

"What the . . . it cannot be!" I gasped.

"Oh yes, Burchard, it is . . . ," said the butler sinisterly.

"But how? What? You . . . you were gone for five hours!"

"Actually, it was more like seven," replied the butler as he stepped toward the stakes.

The butler was covered in rainbow feathers, and his wrinkled face was painted with purple pigment. Given his appearance, it was obvious that the indigenous people had kidnapped him, realized that he fulfilled some sort of mystical prophecy, and made him their king.

"Although I was kidnapped a mere seven hours ago, I fulfilled some sort of mystical prophecy and was made a king!" said the grinning butler.

"Called it," Hawkins and I simultaneously muttered.

"Mr. Ashworth, this is ridiculous! Untie me!" I yelled.

"What about me?" protested my bald companion.

"Didn't you hear me? You have offended Hamer-eek, the Sky God!" croaked the butler, presumably as loud as he could. It was then that a huge elephant came into view, led by a group of villagers.

"I told you there were elephants!" groaned Hawkins.

"First of all, where did these people get an elephant?" I shouted in disbelief.

"They had it imported," replied the butler matter-of-factly.

"Amazon.com," said one of the villagers in broken English.

"Here's another question: Why am I up to my knees in shit?" asked the bald and foul-smelling accountant.

"Your misdeeds are being cleansed by the most sacred substance known to man, the products of Hamer-eek," explained the servant king.

"You mean to tell me that out of all the potential candidates, these people chose an elephant for their sky god?" I questioned with an arched eyebrow. A villager to my left prodded me with a large branch.

"Do not speak until spoken to!" proclaimed the branch-wielding villager.

"Wait, how do you know English?" I questioned, keeping my eyebrow arched.

"Rosetta Stone," responded the villager as he thrust his branch into my ribs.

"What misdeed did I possibly commit?" protested Hawkins. The villagers began whispering amongst themselves.

"You bare the unmistakable mark of baldness, a result of consuming the most sacred bird in the forest: the golden-beaked rainbow finch," explained the villager with the stick. "Now Hamer-eek will cleanse you."

"We really ought to look into Rosetta Stone," I whispered to Hawkins, who nodded in agreement.

"We will now ready the fire," proclaimed another villager.

"Fire? What for?" Hawkins and I shouted in unison. We were then simultaneously jabbed with branches.

"My people are peaceful, but they do operate under Hammurabi's code, so they're going to eat you," explained the butler.

"Hawkins ate a bird, not one of them! Under Hammurabi's code, eating us doesn't make sense!" I protested. The villagers look at each other in confusion, and they began to whisper.

"You foreigners speak sense, but we're still going

to eat you," said the branch-wielding villager.

"Mr. Ashworth! Please help us! We will do anything!" I screamed.

"Will you buy me a new suit?" questioned the butler.

"Yes!"

"And the raise?"

"Let's not get carried away..." I chuckled nervously.

"Burchard!" cried the bald accountant as the villagers began to unearth the stake.

"Fine! The raise too!" I yelled in defeat.

"Well that's just grand!" said the smiling butler as he whipped out his pistol (from God knows where) and fired a warning shot into the sky. The villagers stopped in their tracks.

"My people, you have served me well, but the *time has come to be gone, and though I've helped thee drink a thousand times, it's time to ramble on,*" said the butler as smoke rose from his pistol. The villagers looked at him in confusion.

"I don't think they get the reference . . . ," I whispered to the butler.

"Right," replied the butler as he swiftly cut the rope from my limbs, and soon did the same for Hawkins. I landed with a thud on the ground, but Hawkins landed with a sploosh. The villagers did not like this, and began to scream wildly.

"We'd better run," said the frowning butler.

"Do you know the way out?" Hawkins chimed in.

"Just follow me, and keep up," replied the butler, as his catlike agility returned. I followed the sprinting feathered butler and the bald accountant into the depths of the jungle. The villagers short legs kept them at a distance, and soon they were out of sight.

"I do believe your hair is growing back, Hawkins." The accountant sat down on the sofa in the sitting room. "Thankfully, yes," responded the nearly bald accountant.

"I hope you've forgiven me for lying about the golden-beaked rainbow finch."

"Well it panned out to be quite the adventure!" chuckled Hawkins. Mr. Ashworth walked into the sitting room in his new suit.

"Hello, Hawkins," said the classy butler. "Your hair is growing back nicely."

"Thank you, Mr. Ashworth, you are quite kind—and classy, might I add."

"Mr. Engle, your Rosetta Stone just arrived," said the butler as he produced a package.

"Splendid!" I exclaimed as I grabbed hold of the convenient and easy-to-use language software.

"Burchard, what time is it?" questioned Hawkins.

"About three fifty."

"No, I mean what time period are we in? Also, where are we? I think eating that bird may have caused some severe memory loss. Speaking of which, isn't it odd that the golden-beaked rainbow finch existed after all? Your prophecy came true . . ."

"Never mind that, Hawkins, help me read this registration code—the print is too damned small!"

"Mr. Engle, the Rosetta Stone wasn't the only parcel in the mail. This came as well," said the butler grimly as he handed me a letter with a blood-red wax seal. I quickly opened it and scanned the page. A look of horror took over my face.

"My cousin Bertha is getting married . . . ," I explained in shock. The butler and the accountant gave me a blank stare.

"Hawkins, haven't you always wanted to go to Africa?"

||

3: THE BLACK BUTTERFLY OF BANGLADESH

I topped off my punch glass for the third time in ten minutes. It was a vile concoction of cheap punch and cheaper vodka, but it was certainly the most interesting thing at this after party. The play was dull and colorless, and its after party proved to be strikingly similar. The drink stung my throat, but it made mingling with these industry types bearable. I was just finishing up a conversation with an elderly woman named Bess, who was convinced I was her grandson. She stood alone across the room, her curly, brown hair cascading down her back. She turned and looked directly at me with sparkling brown eyes. Then all of a sudden she began walking in my direction.

"George, dear, I think it's about time you drove me home."

"For the last time, my name is not George—it's Burchard, and I am not, and never have been, your grandson."

"Oh, George, your sense of humor reminds me of your grandfather! Did I ever tell you about the time when he went to the market looking for eggs, and came back with a little kitten?"

"Yes, in fact you told me this irrelevant story not three minutes ago!" I countered, looking through the crowd for the mysterious woman.

"Oh, I'm sorry, dear, I suppose my age has finally gotten the best of me. I'll go fetch us another drink." Bess turned to go just as the mysterious woman appeared. She smiled as she made her way to the spot previously occupied by the annoying and senile woman.

"Hallo . . ." Her cheeks blushed ever so slightly as

she spoke, and her eyelashes danced up and down as she surveyed my face. I felt a sharp tingling pang of nerves, and suddenly I felt as if I were in a sauna. Sweat began to form on my brow—I couldn't think. My heart and my brain seemed to disconnect, and although I reached deep into my bag of verbal wit, the words I pulled out did not help my cause.

"I are ostrich . . . play man?" Those last few cups of punch were certainly not calming my nerves.

"Are you a foreigner?" The woman smiled and blushed.

The way I saw it, I had two options—try to explain my true identity in my questionable current state of mind or pretend to be a foreigner. Given my current state of nerves and questionable blood alcohol level, I decided to go with the latter.

"Yes," I said in what I imagined to be a spot-on Russian accent.

"My name is Melanie."

It was then that Bess returned carrying an empty cup turned upside down. "I've brought you a drink, George!" The elderly woman extended the overturned cup in my direction. I forced a smile and grabbed the shoulders of a man standing next to me.

"George!" I said maintaining the Russian accent as I pulled the surprised man in front of Bess. The ancient woman looked at the confused man thoughtfully, before breaking out into a toothless smile.

"Oh, George, you've grown so tall!" I heard the woman say as I escorted Melanie away from Bess's new grandson.

"If I had a nickel!" Melanie chuckled.

"Yes?" I said with a sweaty smile—my face must've been as red as a tomato.

"It was nice meet you . . ."

"Burchard!" I shouted a little louder than I had intended.

"Good-bye, Burchard . . . ," she said with a smile as she disappeared into the crowd.

"What happened next?" Hawkins asked eagerly as he bit into his frozen chocolate-coated banana.

"I took a cab home, slept off the vodka, and then met you here at the café."

"You know, I haven't been to the Shady Business café since we met here with that assassin all that time ago," Hawkins reported with a mouth full of banana.

"Yes, I wonder what happened to that assassin . . ." It was then that the café's transvestite proprietor approached our table. "You fellas need anything? How are the banana twists? They're named after me, you know."

"Oh yes, we know . . . ," I said as I rolled my eyes.

"My banana twist was just wonderful! Say, I really like what you've done with the café—it looks brand new! Also, this new patio is superb!" observed Hawkins as he finished off his potassium-laden treat.

The café owner then looked at me. "Well after I acquired your grandfather's fortune, I thought I'd spruce the place up a little bit. Anyways, if you boys need my services, you know where to find me . . ." Banana Twist winked at Hawkins before returning into the café.

"Isn't she great?" Hawkins said with an oddly large smile.

"Never mind that, Hawkins, we have much to discuss. Firstly, I am in love with Melanie."

"Melanie?" questioned Hawkins with an arched eyebrow.

"The woman from the after party! I just told you an in-depth account of the events of last night not three minutes ago!"

"Yes, but three minutes ago I was eating a banana twist," replied Hawkins matter-of-factly. He then looked at my plate. "Are you going to finish that?"

"Hawkins, I'm in love!" I shouted at the hungry accountant as I put my head in my hands.

"You know, I've read about love—it's a fairly interesting topic," replied Hawkins as he snatched the banana twist from my plate.

"What have you read?"

"Well, from what I understand, there is only one

way to make a woman fall in love with you . . ." By this time my banana twist had begun its journey through Hawkins's digestive system.

"How?" I shouted. "Out with it, man!"

"In order for a woman to truly fall in love with you, you must place the fabled Black Butterfly of Bangladesh around her neck."

"What the hell is that?" I questioned in dismay.

"The Black Butterfly of Bangladesh is a pendant made of the most sacred stones on the planet. It was said to have been forged in the depths of the Euphrates River before being carried across scorching deserts and lifeless plains by the most fearless warriors of old. The pendant was then hidden in the depths of Bangladesh, in a shrine meant to safeguard the jewel for all eternity. Some say it is guarded by vicious crocodiles that will tear any trespasser limb from limb, but others say it is cursed with a spell that turns any unworthy holder of the pendant into dust. Needless to say, it would be ludicrous to attempt to find and obtain the pendant. Also, do you know that man in the flannel over there? He appears to be listening in . . ."

I looked unblinking at Hawkins with an arched eyebrow.

"No, I know that look, and the answer is no!" said Hawkins in suspicion.

I didn't move a muscle.

"Fine, I'll go with you to Bangladesh, but don't come whining to me when the crocodiles use your limbs as toothpicks!"

"I knew I could count on you, Hawkins!" I exclaimed with a smile. Suddenly I heard a familiar guttural clearing of a throat from behind me. I turned around to see my butler, Mr. Ashworth, standing behind the table with several suitcases.

"Here are your plane tickets and luggage, sir," stated the butler as he handed me the tickets. "Your plane leaves in two hours," finished the butler as he began to walk away.

"Wait, Mr. Ashworth, how did you know?" I questioned in awe. Mr. Ashworth paused and then faced me, his face unmoved.

"I know all things," stated the butler as he turned to leave once again.

The Dhaka airport smelled of spices and feet, but Hawkins and I enjoyed a nice curry dish there before hailing a taxi.

"Where to?" asked the young driver, who appeared to be under twenty years of age.

"Yes, where to, Hawkins?" I asked.

"Well, to be honest, I really didn't think this through," replied the bewildered accountant.

"Hotel Werduhukins it is!" replied the driver in perfect English. Hawkins and I looked at each other in amazement as the cab took off down the road.

The hotel looked more like a crowded house than a business, but it would do. The price was cheap, and I presumed we wouldn't be staying there long. Hawkins and I took our suitcases up a flight of stairs and walked down a hallway until we found the door with a number matching the tag on our key. I opened the door to a small room barely big enough to host the single twin bed and side table occupying the space.

"Looks like we'll have to get cozy, Burchard!" said Hawkins with a smile as he sat down on the bed.

"Never mind that, Hawkins, we should really get around to finding that butterfly pendant!"

"Yes, I think we should start by finding some more curry! It is unwise to search on an empty stomach!" exclaimed Hawkins while putting his hand on his stomach.

"Firstly, we ate not twenty minutes ago. Secondly, why don't we start at that jewelry shop I see across the street," I said while looking out the window. "The shopkeeper is bound to know something about the pendant!"

"Maybe that is not such a good idea . . . ," replied Hawkins nervously.

"Whyever not?" I questioned suspiciously.

"No reason . . . ," countered the fidgeting accountant.

"Very well, let's go!" I exclaimed while making for the door.

The jewelry shop looked fairly cramped and run-down from the outside, yet the interior was anything but. The walls were lined with glass cases containing the most exquisite jewelry I had ever seen. Hawkins did not seem as pleased to be in the shop as I was, and he appeared quite nervous.

"Pull yourself together, Hawkins, we are on the right track! Any jewelry store clerk will most definitely know something about the Black Butterfly of Bangladesh!" It was then that a small well-dressed man came over to us from a back room.

"Burchard, I have a confession to make," said Hawkins sheepishly.

"What's the matter, Hawkins?"

"Well, here it goes . . . There is no Black Butterfly of Bangladesh. I made the whole thing up . . . "

"No Black Butterfly of Bangladesh? But whyever would you lie about such a thing?" I exclaimed, disheartened.

"Well, I wanted to get back at you for tricking me into going to the Amazon in an attempt to find a fictitious bird, but now I feel dreadful." Hawkins looked down at the shop floor. "I'm sorry."

"It's all right, Hawkins. I deserve this. I suppose Melanie will never love me . . ."

"Excuse me, sir, but I couldn't help overhearing that you're looking for the fabled Black Butterfly of Bangladesh," said the classy shopkeeper behind me.

"You know about the Black Butterfly of Bangladesh?" I asked in confusion.

"Follow me . . . ," said the shopkeeper in a whisper as he looked to make sure no one else was around. He then motioned for Hawkins and me to follow him into the back room.

It was small, dusty, and dark; the back room was nothing like the main shop room. The shopkeeper then knelt down and uncovered a safe previously covered by dusty boxes.

After a very complicated combination, the safe opened and revealed a small solitary case. The shopkeeper then stood up and presented the case to Hawkins and myself. He slowly opened the case. Inside was the Black Butterfly of Bangladesh.

"Great Scott! It's the Black Butterfly of Bangladesh!" Hawkins and I gasped in unison.

"Actually, this is just a replica—the real pendant is guarded by the dreadful Crocodile King."

"Damn!" I exclaimed. "How do I obtain the real pendant?"

"You must first make an offering to the king. If he deems it worthy, he will find you and inspect your character. Legend says that if you are truly deserving of the pendant, you will wake with it in your palm."

"Where can we find this Crocodile King?" questioned Hawkins.

"I can take you to him, but there is still the matter of the offering," replied the now nervous shopkeeper. "There is one thing I have yet to mention . . ."

"Yes?" I asked nervously.

"If your offering is not satisfactory, the Crocodile King will slit your throat while you sleep . . ."

"Mother of Zeus!" gasped Hawkins. "Burchard, this was a horrible idea—let's go home."

"No, Hawkins, we must face the terrible Crocodile King. Besides, don't you always carry a pistol in your jacket? If he tries to kill us, we'll simply shoot his crocodile head off!"

"Right!" replied the now courageous Hawkins.

"But we still need an offering." I scratched my chin in thought.

"I think I can help . . . ," replied the shopkeeper.

"I can't believe you bought the most expensive jewel in the store!" noted Hawkins as our rented boat putted down the river.

"It was a small price to pay for the security of knowing my throat won't be slit while I sleep!" I responded gingerly. "And to top it off, you still have that pistol! We are safe, Hawkins!"

The shopkeeper drove our boat further and further down the river, past great plains and small villages. The sun began to set as the boat slowed to a halt. We had reached a small cove with two human skulls on stakes marking the entrance. Hawkins and I looked at each other nervously. As we approached the cove's shoreline, a small shrine came into view.

"There is where you will place your offering," said the shopkeeper, pointing to the eerie shrine. I reached into my pocket for the large diamond I had purchased. I held it in my hand and looked at the large stone momentarily before tossing it onto the shrine. All of a sudden, a large bird swooped down from a tree, screaming with malicious intent.

"The gun!" I yelled at Hawkins. The accountant reached into his coat and produced not a gun, but an old banana twist. The nutritious treat slipped out of his hand and flew toward the shrine as the shopkeeper revved the motor. The boat lurched forward, but the bird's talon scratched Hawkins's arm. Luckily, the bird did not give chase once the boat had left the cove.

"You foreigners are funny!" chuckled the driver. "That was just an osprey!"

"Hawkins! What happened to your gun?" I shouted.

"I thought I had it!" replied the panicked accountant. "I thought the banana twist was the gun!"

"Well, let's just hope that diamond was a satisfactory offering . . . ," I said nervously.

"I'm sure you and your friend will be fine . . . ," said the shopkeeper, but his faltering voice and the beads of sweat on his forehead said otherwise.

"Hawkins, do you think that shopkeeper tricked us?" I asked as I lay on the hotel bed.

"What do you mean?" responded the accountant as he lay on the floor.

"Well, suppose he's going back there right now to take back the diamond we left on the shrine."

"Oh. I didn't even think of that," replied the accountant as he sat up.

"Damn! We've been fooled, Hawkins! This whole trip has been a disaster! Now I'll never be loved. My hopes are dashed; my dream is done; I suppose I'll just wither up into a solitary ball and die . . ."

"Don't say that, Burchard! At least we have each other! You know friendship is the beacon of hope shining on this desolate and unforgiving world, and without it, well . . . I sort of forgot where I was going with that," admitted Hawkins earnestly.

"That's all right, Hawkins, let's just try and get some sleep."

"Right. Good night, Burchard."

"Good night, Hawkins," I said as I turned off the light. " . . . Hawkins?"

"Yes, Burchard?"

"Why did you climb into bed with me?"

"I didn't . . ."

I quickly reached for the light switch. The light revealed a man painted in green scales wearing a crown of crocodile teeth. A black ghoulish mask shrouded his face, but his piercing eyes peered into the depths of my very being.

"Hawkins! The gun!" I yelled.

"I don't have it!"

"Oh yes, I'd forgotten about that . . . Please, Mr. Crocodile King, don't kill me!" I pleaded.

"Yes, please don't kill us!" added Hawkins. The Crocodile King didn't move.

"Well, I mean, if you have to kill someone, you should kill Hawkins! This is all his fault!" I explained. The Crocodile King looked at Hawkins.

"Well it was actually more of a group effort, I mean, the shopkeeper was involved too, you know, if you want to get technical . . . ," replied the fidgeting Hawkins. Then the Crocodile King spoke.

"Well I certainly can't kill anyone I share a banana twist with!" responded a familiar voice.

"It can't be!" I gasped.

"It is!" said Burchard English as he took off the mask.

"You're the Crocodile King?" asked Hawkins, who was trying to conceal his soiled pants.

"I am, indeed, well I mean, it's really just a hobby—I don't want it to define me or anything," responded the Deadly Ostrich.

"But why? How?" I asked in amazement.

"Well, things got pretty hot back home after my most recent escapade at the church, so I decided to wait things out in Bangladesh until they started to cool down. But then I found this sacred butterfly pendant in the river one day, started a rumor, created a legend, and I've been the Crocodile King ever since!" explained the part-time assassin.

"Well, to be honest, I really don't know how to proceed given the most recent development in this saga," I exclaimed honestly.

"How about I give you the pendant if you promise to ship me one hundred banana twists?" countered the Crocodile King.

"Done!" I shouted in joy.

"By the way, the offering of the banana twist was genius! Gutsy, but genius! Most people usually try to offer me some sort of diamond, and I kill those people. Good thing you didn't do that!" Burchard English chuckled. Hawkins and I looked at each other nervously.

"Well, old friend, would you like to come back home with us on the plane tomorrow? I can pay for your ticket!" I offered.

"Thanks, old boy, but my place is here as the Crocodile King. If I were to leave, who else would terrorize the small villages with serial violent crimes?"

"That's a good point . . . ," said Hawkins nervously.

"Well chums, I'd better get going, but it was great to see some familiar faces! Oh, also, there is a man wearing a flannel outside your window watching us— it's kind of creepy." Burchard then got off the bed and headed for the door.

Hawkins and I looked at each other with squinted

eyes.

"Must be a coincidence," muttered Hawkins.

"Wait, I believe this belongs to you . . . ," said the Crocodile King as he retrieved the Black Butterfly of Bangladesh (from God knows where) and placed it in my outstretched hand.

"One more thing," questioned Hawkins. "How did you track us?"

"I trained my pet osprey to implant a GPS tracking device on everyone who leaves an offering. Don't look for it, though, it's deep in your bloodstream by now. Good-bye, gents!" said the eccentric assassin as he left the hotel room.

"All right, Hawkins, here we are, the after party for the latest play by the same bloke whose after party I attended before. Hopefully the guest lists are identical and Melanie will be in attendance," I explained as Hawkins and I entered the party. I looked around the crowded room but Melanie was nowhere to be found.

"Hawkins, can you fetch us some punch? I'm really quite thirsty."

"Sure thing!" responded the accountant as he turned to go. All of a sudden, a familiar voice caught my attention.

"George! You've made it! Oh, I am so glad to see you here!" exclaimed my faux grandmother.

"Hello, Bess . . . ," I said with an audible groan.

"How about a kiss for Granny?"

"How about a drink for Grandson?"

"Oh, you are so clever! I'll be right back with some punch!" said the senile old woman as she turned to leave. It was then that I saw her.

Melanie was just as strikingly beautiful as before, and then, all of a sudden, our eyes met. She flashed her stunning smile and her face lit up like the summer moon. As she began to walk toward me, Hawkins appeared with the punch.

"Here's your drink, Burchard!" said Hawkins

gingerly. I took the cup from his grasp and chugged the contents down in one gulp.

"I've finished it, get me another one!" I whispered.

"Here you can have mine too, I'll just get back in line . . . ," responded the startled accountant. Just as he turned to leave, Melanie appeared before me.

"Hello, Burchard . . . ," she said sheepishly. This time courage filled my lungs with the ability to speak.

"Hello, Melanie, I'm so glad to see you! I actually have something for you." I pulled out the Black Butterfly of Bangladesh from my pocket.

"Oh, George, you shouldn't have!" said the old woman as she dropped the punch at my feet and snatched the pendant with a youthful agility.

"Wait, Bess, no!" I whispered urgently, but the old woman already had the pendant around her neck.

"You remind me of my husband, but he died a long time ago . . . ," Bess crooned as I slowly backed away.

"I've been so lonely, you know . . . I am just wishing for a big, strong man to sweep me off my feet .. ." Bess was getting closer.

"Umm, Bess, I think you have the wrong idea . . . Hawkins!" I shouted. There was really no need to shout—Hawkins was already behind Bess, and plucked the pendant from her neck. He then proceeded to throw it across the room.

"Hawkins! What the hell are you doing?!" I yelled as the Black Butterfly of Bangladesh flew across the room.

"What the—it's that guy! The one who has been following us!" exclaimed Hawkins, pointing to where he'd thrown the pendant. Sure enough, the mysterious flannel-wearing man caught the pendant and ran off. I stood still with my mouth gaping.

"No!" I cried, putting my hands to my head. Both Bess and Melanie looked on in confusion and disbelief. By this time, the whole party had come to a standstill, and everyone was looking at me.

I then turned my gaze to Melanie—she looked at me like I was crazy.

"Look, Melanie, I don't know how to say this,

but I've loved you ever since I first laid eyes on you. I thought the only way to get you to love me was to give you the most beautiful jewel in the whole world, but I see now that love is the real treasure, and I've been a fool. I'm sorry about all this. I hope you can forgive me."

Melanie looked at me in confusion. "What?"

"Oh no, I've made an even bigger fool out of myself!"

"What? I no understand! I'm from Russia!"

"Wait, do you speak English?"

"If I had a nickel," she said gingerly.

"Wait, what do you mean by that?"

"It was nice meet you." She blushed. She then gave me a peck on the cheek. "Good-bye, Burchard." She then turned to go.

As she walked away, Hawkins came up to me.

"What do you think that guy in the flannel is going to do with the Black Butterfly of Bangladesh?

"Never mind that, Hawkins. Let's go get some banana twists."

||

JUST BIRDS

Just Birds was written by Henry and illustrated by Simon Alexander-Adams in the tenth grade. It was a finalist in the B'nai B'rith International Diverse Minds Youth Writing Challenge

Today was the day Bird would leave his nest,
Bird would fly and sing with the rest.

He waited and waited for this day to come.
He waited for Poppa bird to say, "Come on son,
Let's fly today, into the world we'll go!
Oh what a world you'll grow to know!"

But as Bird looked outside his nest,
He saw his colors didn't match the rest.

As a matter of fact there were tons of birds,
Each one different from the next.

Bird said to Poppa bird,
"Why am I different, how can that be?
How are there so many birds in this tree?"
Poppa bird said. . .

"As you can see, the world is filled with others,
Others that come in all shapes and colors.
And today I hope you will see,
It makes no difference if you're red, blue or green,

Because you may ask yourself 'Why, why, why?'
But we're all still just birds,
Just birds in the sky."

And with that Bird was ready to leave,
Ready to leave and ready to see,
All the other birds that live in the tree.

So Poppa held Bird's hand
And they jumped from the nest
And slowly began...

To fly, to fly! Oh how they flew,
Flew past their nest and past other nests too.
Bird was happy to finally flap his wings.
He was so happy he began to sing,

And sing he did all through the sky.
He sang and sang until he heard the cry,
Of the other birds that had caught his eye.

The words that they used confused little Bird,
Bird was concerned with the words he overheard!
"Poppa, I don't want to make a fuss,
But those other birds don't sound like us!"

When Poppa said,
"We may chirp, we may squawk,
But they're all still words,
We may speak differently,
But we're all still birds."

"Poppa tell me about these birds
And what they do,
I think I would like to meet a few!"
"Well," said Poppa bird. . .

"There are birds from Switzerland
And birds from France,
There are birds in this tree
Who prefer to wear pants!

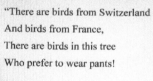

"There are birds from Nigeria
And birds from Peru,
Birds who stand on one foot instead of two!

"There are birds from Mexico
And birds from Brazil,
Birds who like the hot
And birds who like to chill.

"There are birds from Canada, Italy and Japan,
There are birds who like the water
And birds who like the land.

"There are birds who like the night
And birds who like the day,

"There are birds who like to work
And birds who like to play."

"Hey I like to play!" said Bird full of glee,
"Do you think one of these other birds
Would like to play with me?"

"I would like to play!" said a bird nearby.
"I've got tons of games that I think you should try!"
"Games, I love games! He is no different than me!"

"I guess in the end we're just birds in a tree."

EXPIRATION

I slowly let the ashes from my hand.
If expiration is my disease,
then boredom is the plague of man.
She asks me if I'm feeling fine,
I tell her that I am.
Dancing, she keeps me company,
but only for so long.
Twenty years will pass her by
before her fire's gone.
The Earth it turns
as we slowly burn
until ashes we become.
Our legacy lives on in solemn song.

TWISTED IN TIME

The light is gone
and I'm alone,
solitude is a simple joy.
See the kingdom
from the throne.
Dancing smoke keeps company,
but only for so long.
The earth it turns,
as I slowly burn,
until ashes I become.
My legacy lives on
in solemn song.

"In summary, this year was about doing my best to channel the values of Henry Mackaman every day of my waking life."

-Monica Nigon

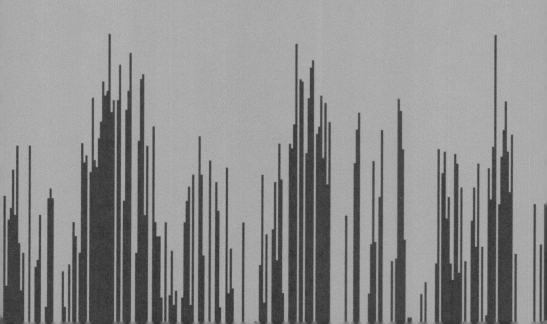

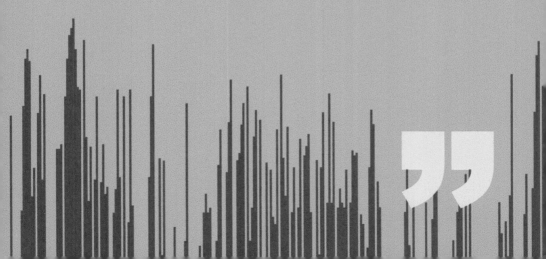

"Henry's life changed all of us—even those who never met him. And he keeps making us better, every day."

-Andrew Lisowski

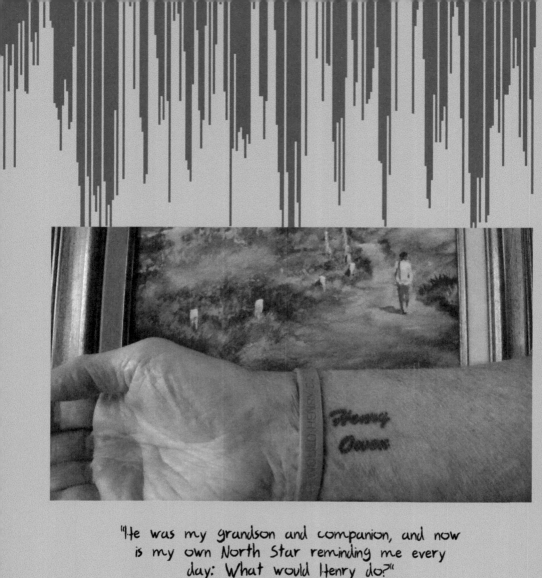

"He was my grandson and companion, and now is my own North Star reminding me every day: What would Henry do?"
-David Strand, Henry's grandpa

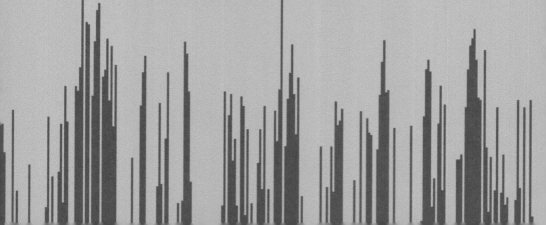

Henry's mom, Meredith, with the winners of the Henry Douglas Mackaman Creative Writing Prize. (From left to right, Kayleigh Norgord, Meredith Leigh, and Renee Jerome.)

RUSALKA

By Johanna Lepro-Green
2017 Winner of the Henry Douglas Mackaman
Creative Writing Prize

The newscaster had called the algae *tiny plants with a toxic punch* and this turn of phrase empowered Dorset more than any therapist ever had. When she was in bed she rolled these words around her mouth like a piece of hard candy until she fell asleep and had shitty dreams. During the day, Dorset rubbed her pregnant belly and stared at the algae blooms that turned the whole lake green. She'd seen on the news that the state was monitoring its growth with a satellite supplied by NASA, and it gave her great comfort to know it was there, bearing witness to the rot.

No one could swim there that summer, not dogs or wives or kids. The beach was closed. The dogs curled up sullen on the couch and watched *The Real Housewives*. The teens got high in unfinished basements damp with possibility. They walked down to the lake to poke the soft, piled-up fish with a stick.

The wives and kids pretended there had never been a lake at all. They went to the public pool instead. The toddlers knew nothing. They had never seen the lake and so they didn't miss it, thought the pool *was* it. They wore floaties and tight caps in bright colors and sat dreamy in the shallow end. In the deep end the kids clung to the mossy edge and the preteens pushed each other underwater in a ritual of nascent desire. The wives examined their stretch marks and their split ends and thought about all of their products lined up on the shelves behind their bathroom mirrors: the Aztec Secret clay masks, the cleansers in frosted bottles, the oatmeal moisturizer, and the Bloomingdale's sample of Crème de la Mer, born from the sea. They read bestsellers, while stretched out on beach towels, where the twist always was that women could be as evil as men.

All of them liked it when someone pooped in the

water. It was the unspoken bond they shared. It gave the day character. They liked it when the teenage lifeguards evacuated the pool with a world-weary announcement through the megaphone. Sometimes the lifeguards were their children or their older siblings and it made them proud to see them at work. The children liked to stand shivering in towels and stare at the turd floating peacefully in the pool. The wives liked it when the most virile male lifeguard caught it in his mammoth white net and held it triumphantly over his head like a trophy while everyone clapped.

When the threat had been deactivated, the lifeguards blew their whistles in tandem and it could all begin again. The children jumped in from all sides and appreciated everything they had taken for granted only a few minutes before: the clouded view of legs kicking underwater, the soothing repetition of *Marco! Polo!*, the sharp sting of chlorine in their nose.

Dorset hated the pool. She hated listening to Joan Osborne ask if God was one of us from the booming speakers at the snack bar. She hated how ordinary it made her feel, like a speck or a smear of waste on some forgotten cosmic plane.

She especially hated the pool since her separation. Her soon-to-be ex-husband, Greg had been a swimmer up until he graduated from college. He had compressed and condensed the events of his life to the time spent in the pool and his time out of it, and each decision he made was governed by the rules of the sport.

She met him during her sophomore year of college, dragged along to a home meet by her roommate, who had been dating the equipment manager, a failed swimmer from a swimmer family. Now that it was over, she realized she hadn't fallen in love with Greg, but with his dedication to something so unambiguous and precise. Her own life lacked coherence, each decision she made a mistake made from the mistake before it. Loving Greg gave her access to order, a set of secondhand guidelines she could follow as though they belonged to her. After graduation, he'd had to quit swimming. He'd never been the best athlete, and he'd injured his rotator cuff during his last season. There was no team to belong to, no more morning practices or weekends spent in commuter vans. He became sluggish and unmoored, wandering through their shared apartment in a red bathrobe and complaining of a persistent low-grade fever.

They dated on and off for six years. Sometimes Dorset dumped him for another athlete: a somber runner who put Band-Aids over his nipples before a race, an ultimate frisbee player with a Napoleon complex, the embarrassing four months with an amateur MMA fighter who believed in Jesus and the Iraq War. Sometimes Greg was the one doing the dumping: he met a girl swimmer from Knox College, he'd had an emotional affair with a waitress who made him feel alive for the first time on land, and once, worst of all, he had cited no reason, he just wanted to be alone. They came together for the last time on a hot weekend in August, and returning to him made Dorset feel like she was re-entering a chrysalis.

Greg started swimming again at the beginning of the end of their marriage. At first, she went with him to the pool each weekend. They woke up at dawn and drove silently there. She watched him from a lawn chair that left red marks on the underside of her ass, pinching crust from the almond of her eyes. It was at the pool that Greg first met Ula, on a morning Dorset had decided to stay home. She saw Ula after the affair had started, swimming merciless laps in the lane next to Greg while her daughter Nastya stood unblinking in the shallow end like a Ukrainian JonBenét Ramsey, a lost porcelain doll.

She reminded Dorset of when she dated a farmer's son as a teenager, who wooed her by whispering off-color jokes into her ear during remedial math. When he first saw her naked, arms stretched out and welcoming on the floor of his family's polygonal barn, he stared in awe at her and told her she looked like the corn husk dolls his little sister made in front of the fireplace at night. "They have no faces," Dorset said to him, and he curled up around her like a newborn to put his mouth around her nipple.

"You don't need to come here with me," he told her one day as he toweled off, a few months after the affair started.

"Sometimes it's nice just to have some time on my own."

"But I like it," she told him. "It's our thing."

There was a part of her that believed that if she had gone with him the morning he met Ula that none of it would have happened, that she'd still be floundering in her old life with him.

But it was at the pool that Dorset met Bobby, back home for the summer before his final year of college. She'd been watching the algae being carried through the water on the lake when her neighbor Marsha had come up behind her and said "boo!" and asked her to come swimming. Ever since the separation, Marsha had been worried about Dorset. The night before, she'd watched her sobbing on her riding lawnmower while she sat sneaking a smoke on her back porch, and Marsha wanted to help, provide her with fluids, pep talks, a daily routine.

"No thanks," Dorset said. "I've got things to do."

She held up a ham sandwich and a library book about World War II.

"You know this is toxic, right?" Marsha asked, her arm motioning to the sludge on the lake. "It's closed for a reason."

"Only from prolonged contact with skin," Dorset answered. "Or if you swallow the water."

"The Richardson's dog died from it, before it got bad," Marsha said, coming to sit next to her on the bench. "He went into a coma. They have a little gravestone next to their lilac bushes."

Dorset opened the plastic baggie and took out her ham sandwich, offering Marsha one half. She waved it away with her hand.

"I can't eat here. All these toxins make me dizzy."

Dorset put the other half back into the baggie, and Marsha leaned in close to her, her breath astringent from mouthwash.

"Please come to the pool with me. It'll be fun. A girls' day!"

She pouted and then mimed crying, her hands in two fat fists near her eyes.

"I don't have a swimsuit that fits," Dorset said,

motioning to her stomach.

Marsha jumped up, undeterred.

"Come over. I've got a few from when I was pregnant with the twins."

Dorset and Marsha walked slowly to the pool, their flip-flops hitting the ground with a humiliating *thomp thomp*. Marsha let her borrow a maternity swimsuit she'd worn on a cruise through the Bahamas before her own divorce, a magenta one-piece with a small, ruffled skirt. Dorset felt ugly and free because of it. She was nothing, a void, a constipated vessel for future life. Marsha was wearing a yellow bikini that showed off her C-section scar.

When they got to the pool, it was packed. All the lawn chairs had been taken by wives who had gotten there hours before, and the space on the grass was so engorged and stratified with people that it resembled the alluvial floodplains she used to study at work. Marsha led her by the hand through the mass to the top of a small hill where they leaned against a chain link fence and searched for an open spot down below.

"Look!" Marsha said, and pointed to a thin strip of cement close to the diving board. "Come on, Dorse," she said, and they walked down until they reached it.

"Shit," Marsha said. "There's only room for one towel."

"You stay," Dorset said, feeling relieved. "I'll head home."

Marsha gripped her arm.

"No! It's a girls' day," she said. "I'm keeping my word."

She laid her towel down, sat, and then tapped the shoulder of the boy sitting next to her, talking to a chubby, cheerless preteen who was methodically organizing a pile of loose grass in front of her. He was wearing the kind of swim trunks she'd seen in catalogues geared toward Midwestern boys who fantasized of being surfers, a half-moon of acne flared out along the top of his back. He turned around.

"Hey," he said to her, and then looked at Dorset, his gaze pulling up past her legs and belly to her breasts, which were the largest they'd ever been. She felt herself growing sharper, just like that. He grinned and shielded his eyes from the sun. "Hey."

"Mind scooching over a little?" she said, and then pointed to Dorset. "My friend needs a place to put her towel."

"Of course!" he said, and then rubbed the girl's shoulder. "Move over."

The girl scooted her butt a full centimeter before stopping and resuming her organizing. The boy rolled his eyes.

"Yo. Move."

The girl screamed. Dorset laughed in surprise. The other visitors near them turned around and looked at all of them like they were a unit, some sort of strange alien family. Marsha took a step back and began picking at her nails.

"Don't tell me what to do," the girl said, and then got up. "I'm outta here."

She picked up her towel and waterlogged book, placed them in a stained tote bag, and left. Dorset and Marsha watched her walk away until she was just a dot on the land, swinging the fence shut behind her. They looked at the pile of grass she left behind. So this is what they had to look forward to.

The boy grimaced, and then stood up and pulled his towel to the space where the girl had been.
"Sorry about that," he told them. "My sister. She's crazy."
"All women are," Marsha said, and then winked. She motioned for Dorset to sit down between them.
Marsha and Bobby introduced themselves to each other, and then Marsha placed her hand possessively on Dorset's shoulder.

"And this is Dorse," she said.

"Dorset," she corrected her.

"It's a nickname," Marsha said, releasing her.

"Nice to meet you," Bobby said, and then held out his hand for Dorset to shake. Dorset gripped it loosely and he flopped it around like a fish.

"You have a weak handshake," he told her.

"I don't need to have a strong handshake," she told him.

"You're less likely to get hired," he told her. "It conveys a lack of authority."

"Maybe that's what I want to convey," she told him. "A lack of authority."

He laughed. Marsha pushed her hand past Dorset.

"I've got a great handshake," she said, and Bobby took her hand. She squeezed.

"My bones!" he said, and pulled his hand away, shaking it as though he was playing pretend with a child.

"See?" Marsha said to Dorset. "I wasn't lying."
Bobby looked at Dorset conspiratorially, a glance so quick that she didn't know if she'd imagined it.

"You in college, Bobby?" Marsha asked, spreading her legs out in front of her.

"Just finished my junior year. Civil Engineering."
Marsha whistled. "And what are you doing for the summer?" she asked.

"Lawn care. My dad owns a landscaping business. And hanging out with my sister." He looked toward the exit where the girl had left."Or trying to."

Dorset spread her legs out in front of her too. Marsha kept talking. "Any of your friends from high school home?"

He shrugged. "We kind of grew apart. They all hang out. I'm just not into it."

He looked at Dorset's belly. "How far along?" he said, and then blushed. "If you don't mind me asking."
"One hundred years," she said, and Bobby laughed.

"Girl or a boy?"

"I don't know yet. It's a surprise."

"Do you want one more than the other?"

Bobby pressed his hairy leg against hers casually. She leaned into him.

"Well I went to this fortune teller when I was visiting L.A. and she told me that if it's a girl she'll be stillborn. She said I'll wrap her in newspaper and bury her in the walls of my attic."

Bobby looked surprised for a moment and Marsha forced out a strained chuckle. She grinned at him. She suddenly felt drunk, fermented. She reclined on her arms and soaked in the sun.

"And then what will you do?"

 She sat up again.

"Then I'll wander the rooms of my house and wail for one hundred more years."

"And if it's a boy?"

"He'll require three AA batteries. If I press the pads of his hands he'll laugh or cry. If I pull the cord on his back he'll piss or poop. He'll never grow up and if I roll over him on accident he won't die."

"Dorse!" Marsha said, warning her. She turned to Bobby.

"She's going through a divorce. She's a little loopy right now."

"Shut up, *Marsh*," Dorset said. "I'm fine."
Marsha collapsed into herself, wounded. She took out a nail file and turned away from them.

"You're crazy," Bobby told her. He looked excited. She felt him rising toward her. Dorset whispered in his ear.

"All women are."

A whistle rang out. A lifeguard yelled into his megaphone.

"Everyone out of the pool! We've got a floater."

At first Bobby was scared that he would fuck the baby out of her.

"I'm scared I'm going to fuck the baby out of you," he confessed to her after they ditched Marsha at the corner of her block. He stood embarrassed and naked in the middle of her living room, couldn't look anywhere except for at his toes sinking down into the plush blue carpet. She had to sit him down on her new couch and tell him all about the amniotic sac, the strong muscles of the uterus, the thick mucus plug that seals the cervix and helps guard against infection. He nodded like he was in a lecture hall, took it all in like a sponge. When she was done, he cupped her face with his hands and kissed her slowly, and she snaked her tongue over the fillings on his molars. She reached her hand and curled it around his shaft and he closed his eyes in mock defeat.

"I can't believe this is happening," he told her. She got down on her knees.

"Well, it is."

They did it everywhere and in every way. They did it cowgirl style and reverse cowgirl style and on the washer and in his childhood bedroom when no one else was home. They did it in his sister's bedroom while her turtle watched and in Dorset's bedroom with her almost ex-husband staring at them from a wedding picture in a heavy metal frame. They did it soapy in the shower and in Dorset's living room with her face pressed up against a wall. They did it until their legs shook so much they had to press against them with flat hands. They did it until they drooled.

When Dorset was with him, she was buoyant, contorted, leaping. She was a salmon out of water, lit up and raw by him. Her hair was always sticky with sweat. She listened to him while he told her about his failed Accutane treatment, his runaway dog, his sort-of girlfriend back at school who was afraid of heights, and food, and banana slugs. She told him lies.

When Dorset and Bobby were apart, she sat on her bench at the lake. She was nauseous and empty. She tried to think up names for her baby but she felt fuzzy, her brain thick with fatigue. She stared at the algae that grew thicker each day and ate her ham sandwich and learned facts about World War II that she told him when they were together again. "Did you know that a number of air crewman literally died of farts?"

A few weeks after she started seeing Bobby, she saw Ula and Greg at the Prairie View Mall. They were eating orange chicken with one hand and holding hands with the other. There was an engagement ring on Ula's thin, witchy finger. On the floor were two shopping bags brimming with things. She felt sick. The baby kicked.

She began to drive to Ula's work. She worked as a nurse

in a pediatrician's office off the highway, in one of those nondescript business parks that made Dorset feel like she'd been lied to about the American Dream. Ula was good at her job and had worked hard to get it. Dorset knew this because Greg had told her when he confessed to the affair.

"She had to fight to graduate, with a little girl at home, no family to support her," he told her. "She really went through a lot."

Dorset spent hours there. She kept her car running and listened to some third-rate radio therapist blabbing about marriage and divorce and happiness. Sometimes she went inside and stood in the doorway to watch the children play on the floor, stuffy with phlegm. The mothers smiled at her and her pregnant belly and asked her how far along she was.

"One hundred years," Dorset said, and they laughed. Once Ula came out with a clipboard, saw her there, and disappeared behind a door. Another nurse appeared a moment later and called out a name and then gave Dorset a look so punishing that for the rest of the day she felt hollowed out, like the rind of a cantaloupe. One afternoon, Dorset was sitting in the parking lot of the office with her windows open. Her AC unit was broken and she was sweating, the spine of her t-shirt soaking wet. Ula walked outside. She stared at Dorset through the windshield and Dorset pretended she didn't see her. She played with the dial on the radio and thought about death.

Ula walked over to her quickly. She tried to lock the door but Ula was too fast. She opened it, easing into the passenger seat like they were old friends. Dorset gripped the wheel and stared straight ahead, as though she hadn't noticed her arrival.

"You have something to say to me?" Ula asked.

"No," Dorset said. "Nothing. Nada. Zilch."

Ula released a sigh and let her head rest on the seat. Dorset turned. She could see her split ends, the small mole on the right side of her forehead. She was wearing scrubs decorated with happy, hopping frogs. It disappointed Dorset to realize that she would trust her with her baby.

"I hate you," Dorset said.

Ula took a pack of cigarettes out of her breast pocket.

She lit one and blew it out the window, releasing a sloppy puff of smoke.

"Can I give you some advice?"

"No," Dorset said. "Yes."

"You heard of Oxana Oleksandrivna Malaya?"

"No," Dorset said.

"Back in Ukraine, she was big news. Grew up feral. Raised in a kennel with dogs. Parents drank too much vodka. When she was found by authorities, she was seven-and-a-half years old. Could not speak. Ran around on all fours. Barked. Slept on the floor. Took care of her body like dog. She licked her wounds."

Ula hands Dorset the cigarette and she takes a small drag. She hadn't smoked since before she'd been married.

"Now she works at a farm milking cows. She did an interview with the press. Loves her boyfriend and hates when people call her dog girl. She has a new life."

Ula looks at Dorset and she motions for the cigarette.

"You have to kill the idea of yourself," Ula says. "Do you understand?"

"You stole my husband," Dorset said. "You stole my life."

They sat in silence, trading the cigarette back and forth.

"You have fake tits," Dorset said.

"You think I have no history? You think I haven't suffered?"

"I didn't say that."

"When I was growing up, we all had the same things. The whole city. Everything was made by the same manufacturer. We had the same backpacks and the same toilet paper and when we drank tea at someone else's house it was with the same cups we had at home."

"I'm dead," Dorset said. "He killed me."

"You did that to yourself."

"Fuck you," Dorset said.

"You remind me of a *rusalka*," Ula said. "The spirit of drowned girls who have been betrayed by a husband or a lover. They seek revenge upon the living by drowning other people."

"I have to plug my nose when I swim," Dorset told her.

"I know," Ula said. "Greg told me."

Ula opened the car door and stepped outside.

"Don't tell him I let you smoke."

She closed the door and leaned in the open window.

"And don't come here again," she told Dorset.

"Unless it's for pediatric care."

Dorset rolled up the window. Ula stood in the parking lot and watched her until she drove away.

When Dorset was eight months along, Greg met her in the lobby of her doctor's office for a prenatal checkup. He was wearing cargo shorts and a polo shirt she'd never seen before.

"You look stupid," she told him, walking past him and through the door.

They sat two chairs apart in the waiting room, reading old magazines with out-of-date celebrity gossip. When the nurse called them in they walked single file into the doctor's office. Greg stepped out of the room while she pulled on the paper robe, knocking and waiting for her go-ahead before re-entering. He sat on a chair and stared at his phone while she sat on the examining table. After the nurse took her blood pressure and weight, the doctor came in, cheery and distant.

"How's it been since your last visit?" he asked Dorset.

"Bad. I'm scared the baby is going to come out a hard plastic doll."

The doctor looked over at Greg.

"Is she kidding?" he said. Greg looked at her.

"Yes," Dorset said. "She's kidding."

The doctor put on a pair of latex gloves.

"Any contractions? Swelling? Headaches?"

"Heartburn. So bad sometimes I think I'm on fire."

Greg perked up.

"Ula said that heartburn means it's going to be a hairy baby," he said.

Dorset started to cry.

"Oh crap, I'm sorry," he said. She willed him to get up from his chair and reach for her. And he did, but stopped an inch away from her and hovered until the doctor said he could sit back down.

"Fun fact," the doctor said, as he pressed with his

foot to make the head of the table flat. "A baby's first stool is actually the digested remains of their own body hair."

Dorset cried again. The doctor said maybe it was better if Greg stepped out and came back in at the end of the appointment, when Dorset was dressed. Greg left quickly, as though he was relieved to have an excuse to leave.

After he was done examining her, the doctor motioned for her to sit up and she did, clutching the paper robe tight against her. He pulled up a metal stool and looked down at his chart.

"How are you feeling?" he asked Dorset. Then he looked up at her. "Emotionally."

"Strange," she told him. "Excavated. Lonely."

He nodded and wrote something down on his chart.

"We've got to watch out for this," he told her. "I want you to try and be aware of your feelings. Especially after birth. We should get you on something."

She looked over at the door and imagined Greg sitting in his foreign polo shirt on the other side.

"But isn't that normal? After everything I've been through?"

"It can be normal," he told her, standing up. "But that doesn't mean it's not important."

Bobby broke up with her the day before he was supposed to go back to school. He knocked on her door and she opened it wearing red lingerie that made her look like a slutty Santa Claus.

"It's not really breaking up," he told her. "Since we were never really together."

"Since we were never really together," Dorset repeated.

"Exactly," he said. "You're so cool. I'm so glad you get it."

"It was a fling," Dorset said. "It was sex."

Bobby took her hands in his.

"I'm so thankful to have known *you*," he told her, like she was on her deathbed.

They stared into each other's eyes. The baby kicked hard and Dorset flinched.

"No," she said. "I'm so thankful to have known you."

Before he left, she offered him a slice of lasagna from her fridge. He ate it fast and cold, standing up against the island in her kitchen.

The next morning, Dorset sleepwalked. Sleepwalking had been a problem for her as a kid. Her mother had been forced to put a series of monstrous padlocks on their doors and windows to keep her from going outside until she mysteriously grew out of it at age thirteen. Occasionally it reappeared during times of stress. When she learned of her father's death during a vacation out West three years before, she had broken through a glass patio door at a Holiday Inn and had woken up on the lawn in front of the hotel, the shards of glass leaving a series of tiny scars along her palms.

She was barefoot, wearing a ratty, sleeveless nightgown her mother had purchased for her as a gift a few years before. She walked asleep down her stairs and out her front door, leaving it wide open behind her. Marsha saw her from her kitchen window as she packed her children's lunches for camp and waved to her, but Dorset kept walking, slow and determined. It was only afterwards, when Marsha heard about what had happened, did she put the two events together.

Dorset woke up at the edge of Bobby's block. She felt savage and scared and separated from her body, as though she was watching herself from a branch on the oak tree above her. She brought her hand slowly to her mouth and wiped away the drool that was pooling from the edges of her lips. She brought her hand in front of her and squeezed it in and out. She took the other hand and did the same thing. She did this until she felt herself returning, and then she turned and saw Bobby across the street. She felt like a Neanderthal who had somehow been plopped into the future. She was suddenly more aware than she ever had been that everyone she knew was descended from monkeys. It was far out.

His sort-of girlfriend, whom she had seen from a series of pictures she'd found online, was helping him pack boxes into her car. She was thin, so thin it made Dorset suicidal, the bones of her collarbone jutting from her like a taunt. The sort-of girlfriend noticed her first, and pointed at her frozen on the sidewalk.

"Is that lady okay?"

Dorset imagined placing a banana slug on that collarbone, letting it crawl up the underside of her neck.

"Jesus," Bobby said. "That's my neighbor."

He ran over to her and grabbed her hard by the crook of her arm.

"What are you doing here?"

"I'm seeing you off," Dorset said, stepping toward him with glazed eyes.

"You need to go home," he told her, glancing at the sort-of girlfriend. He spoke quietly into her ear. "You really need to go home."

He turned to the sort-of girlfriend. "Hey," he said. "I'm going to walk her home."

The sort-of girlfriend took a step toward them, and Bobby pulled Dorset a step back.

"Should we call a doctor? Is something wrong? Is she sick?"

Bobby shook his head. "She does this all the time."

He twirled his index finger in a circle around his ear, and Dorset laughed.

"All women are crazy!" she said to the sort-of girlfriend, who looked frightened and sad. Dorset began to stomp around like a marching band conductor. "ALL. WOMEN. ARE. CRAZY!"

She ran up to the sort-of girlfriend and the sort-of girlfriend yelped. She pressed the sort-of girlfriend against the window of her car.

"You're crazy too," she told the sort-of girlfriend. She twirled in a circle. "Isn't it divine?"

Bobby came behind her and trapped her in a bear hug and the sort-of girlfriend slipped away from her and to the front lawn.

"She's insane," she yelled to Bobby. "She's really insane."

Dorset fought against Bobby's grip as he carried her down the block.

"What about FEMINISM?" she yelled to the sort-of girlfriend. "What about women supporting other women? Traitor! Judas!"

She struggled until they reached her front steps. Her door was wide open and all the lights were on. He set her on her new couch, which wasn't so new anymore. There was a small stain on the arm where she'd spilled spaghetti. She grew limp and sank into the cushions. He sank next to her.

"What the fuck?" he said, rubbing his face with his hands. "What the fuck?"

Her nightgown rode up to reveal her belly. It was so big and tight. He reached for it, and then pulled away.

On the last day of summer, Dorset's water broke. It happened while she watched HGTV in the middle of the night. It soaked her not-so-new couch and made a puddle on her plush carpet and she knew it was coming. She got up to call Greg. He wanted to be there if she wanted him to be. She let his phone ring once before she hung up.

She thought about calling Marsha, but she hated the name Dorse. It reminded her of the boys who snapped her bra in seventh grade. And she was worried Marsha would make the invitation all about her, pretend that they were something they weren't. As though they were allies in the trenches when they weren't anything at all to one another.

She looked up the number for a taxi. She imagined the driver weaving in and out of traffic seamlessly, wearing one of those corny newsboy caps and smoking a cigarette. She groaned. She felt herself contract. She walked slowly upstairs and to her bedroom, where she bent down to open the bottom drawer of her dresser. Inside was the magenta swimsuit with the ruffled bottom that Marsha had let her borrow a few months before. She put it on.

She looked around at all of the things that were hers but not really. The creams and the lotions and the Bloomingdale's samples of Crème de la Mer from the sea. She looked at the wedding picture on the dresser and the red lingerie falling out of the drawer. She thought about Ula as a little girl, all of that desolate sameness.

She found her flip-flops thrown in the tangle of the closet and put them on too. She packed a pair of scissors and a gauze sponge and a baby blanket and a baby hat. She went outside and walked until she reached the lake. She sat on her bench and looked out at it. At night, the water appeared radioactive, the algae a velvety circle of neon green. Dorset took off her flip-flops and dropped her bag and left them on the beach. She waded into the water. It was warm and calm, made her feel like she was crawling in Earth's bathtub. The ruffle in her skirt puffed up as she moved deeper, and she swore that the pondweed that clung to her legs was conscious, wrapped around her in longing. There was a small spot in the middle of the lake where the moon reflected back in on itself—a small space free of algae. She waded toward it.

When Dorset was a teenager, she liked to lock herself in her best friend's bathroom. The countertop was messy with dried-out lip gloss, flat irons, curlers in various states of disrepair, and an obscene collection of body spray her friend's older sister had stolen from Victoria's Secret. There were waterlogged magazines near the edge of the bath and a collection of underwear piled behind the door. It was muggy and smelled like chemicals. She felt like she was on a movie set, as though someone had been paid to place those things here, in those precise positions. In the bathroom, surrounded by those objects, Dorset had felt dislodged from herself.

The displacement was alternately comforting and eerie. She felt somehow less and more *girl*—that elusive categorization that could be felt just by being in a place where real girls lived. Back then, she had begun to feel like she was failing at being one. There seemed to be some essential piece of her that was missing: the kind of permanent deficiency that she had unsuccessfully tried to fix by learning how to do French braids and giving one-and-a-half clinical hand jobs.

Dorset's uterus tightened and she bent over in pain. The edges of her hair hit the water, and when she stood up again, small drops fell on her shoulders. She placed her arms out and took a deep breath, and then pulled them in again. The algae moved slowly against her in a lazy wave and she swore she felt it through her swimsuit, her skin growing thick with moss. She continued walking until she could only stand on her tiptoes. She saw the open water before her, too far away to reach. So she walked backwards until her feet were flat on the ground and prepared to give birth. She pulled her hair into a ponytail and karate chopped the air, puncturing the silence of the lake with a convincing "hi-ya!" She took a handful of algae between her fingers and let it melt into her like butter. She plugged her nose and went underwater and opened her eyes and saw nothing but a fleece of endless green.

She thought about Greg bent over the bathtub in the first apartment they shared together, shaving his legs for a swim meet. She thought about Bobby sleeping in his dorm room, his girlfriend and all of her fears wide awake next to him. She thought about Ula with her baby and how she would grow to love it too. She floated in the water and stared at the moon and she felt herself harden in preparation.

She sang ancestral songs passed down through generations, like "Hit Me Baby One More Time" and "Once in a Lifetime."

"This is not my beautiful house!" she sang to no one. "This is not my beautiful wife!"

She stood up and bore down. There was pain. Immeasurable surges of pain that coursed through her like a current. It took her to far-off places, a kind of cosmic déjà vu. She traveled somewhere else and then came back. It was far out.

She pushed. She pushed again. She pushed again, and again, and again, until she said to no one that she couldn't push anymore, and no one pushed back. She felt the algae move in, the prodding of a soft wave. She pushed once more.

It came out and she pulled it from the water. Everything was silent. She pressed it into her chest. She stared up at the moon and the stars and the satellite whose job was to bear witness to the rot and she felt it bloom against her, open its tiny fists.

HAPPIEST PLACE ON EARTH

By Renee Jerome
2016 Winner of the Henry Douglas Mackaman
Creative Writing Prize

I get sick of the whirring of my mechanical mind.
Sometimes I think George Washington understands,
but we're not lonely for the same people or places. We
repeat the things we miss over and over, until we know
each other by heart, but there's no replacement for
home. When you're not there nothing exists, so when
I tied my heart to my wife who died in an asylum, and
my lost son who sent her there, I exiled myself to a
phantom existence. I rely on a shadow of a heart, which
circulates poorly and creates a dull, deoxygenated ache.

I miss places I've never been.

I was born in a workroom in a polyester top hat.
At first I thought I'd just woken up from a dream, or
maybe into a dream, but when I tore at my hair it came
away to reveal a metal brick stuck in my brain like a
bullet. As far as I knew, I fell asleep next to Mary Todd
on a normal evening. But sideways to that, overlapping
it a little, I remembered my head splitting open and
spilling on the floor. I don't hold with liars, but it's
becoming harder and harder to figure out what's true.

I was sitting upright when I was born. Above the
door a blue plastic sign read, "A dream is a wish your
heart makes," in curly white letters. I peeked through
the window in the door, but all I could see was bumpy
off-white, like the walls and ceiling. The door was
locked from the outside, so I perched on the small

bench and waited. Finally the door rattled, and despite having won the Civil War, I jumped. I had no idea whether I should feel threatened, but even so I tensed up on the tidy bench. But then the door banged aside, and a frazzled, pudgy man in a white shirt was stuffing his key into the pocket of his jeans. "Eight-oh-three?" he asked nervously, and for a sickening moment I thought he was addressing me. But then he continued, "Or eight-oh-four, maybe? There was traffic," he added. He took a deep breath, forced a smile, and said, "It's my first day."

I stared at him for several moments. "My hat's wrong," I finally said.

His smile vanished.

He introduced himself as Andrew, and began quizzing me on my past. We ran over the basics and I answered it all very easily, but I hated the way that the words drifted to my speech centers, like flotsam from an unexplored sea. It seemed unreasonable for an entire person to be hidden inside my skull without my knowing, but he emerged circuit by circuit, lighting up the memories in the shadowy recesses of my mind. The uneven mix of happy and sad moments was so overwhelming my brain seemed ready to short-circuit. Andrew assured me that any uncomfortable sensations in my head or behind my eyes were just my mind booting up, brand new machinery clicking together and creating some friction. I could relax, because all the people and places filling up my mind were long gone.

"Rebooting, don't you mean?" I asked.

"No . . . ," Andrew said slowly, and flapped his hands and said, "We'll get back to that, Mr. President."

We discussed my death in 1865, which was now well over three hundred years ago. I told Andrew that I was murdered by a strange man in a theater, on what should have been a pleasant evening after a long, bloody war. He nodded, and made a mark on his notepad. I told Andrew that my wife died, as well. That she died alone in an asylum unable to say where or who she was, the last mark of the insane. Andrew assured me that it was long, long ago. I told him I was born in a log cabin in 1809, and that my mother died nine years later. I didn't tell him, but I remembered, that the night she ascended to heaven it was like I'd never seen a sunset. The sky caught fire like never before, and each blade of grass and each cloud in the sky were perfect in every detail. Every night for a whole year she painted heaven red and orange, her celestial masterpiece, and every night I cried as I watched it fade to black.

Andrew asked me what I was, and I mustered my courage and voiced the suspicion creeping in the back of my mind—the part of my mind familiar to me, anyway.

"I am a robot," I said firmly.

"An animatronic," corrected Andrew. "And do you know where you are?"

Mickey Mouse, Cinderella's Castle, and fat tourists in sandals were all trying to find their way to my tongue. "In the happiest place on earth," I finally said. "That's what they tell us," said Andrew, and laughed.

A month later I met my coworkers. By then both fine and gross motor control were running smoothly, so I could shake hands with fifty-three presidents, Martin Luther King Jr., and Virginia Woolf without any errors, like ripping their hands off or punching them in the chest. As we exchanged greetings, I couldn't help picturing what'd be left if you stripped them down to their skeletons. Not just the fake memories and the fake personality and the polyester top hats, but the synthetic skin and the artificial breathing mechanism, the beard and the polished shoes. That afternoon we were all in the President's Wing, one quiet, blue corridor like the next. We roam through the halls indiscriminately, and with miles of dirt between ourselves and the sun we still stop to ask each other why it's so dark.

I learned from the other presidents what I had been manufactured to do. I am a Disneyland animatronic: electronic entertainment. It is my job to teach people about our past, but I've learned that they don't want history or politics so much as they want stories. So I start with "Once upon a time," which in this case is "On February 12, 1809." I pour out all the memories that burst into my head: the moment I was born, the little log cabin and the lost mother, and the year that she gave him a glowing sky. I tell them that Mary Todd had small, delicate hands and feet and warm eyes. In the dark, underground rooms these stories burn like that celestial masterpiece, and together we pour fuel on the flames. I give them all my memories and they give me their round and wistful eyes in return.

I've seen the sky once. When I moved from the building I was built in to this one I had to hike up to the surface with Andrew, and we made the short walk to Building B with trembling fingers. The ground shudders more than shakes on the surface, and the sky above is not blue or orange but gray with ashes. Eventually the chaos has to filter down, and it won't matter then whether I know which hall I'm in. I took note of the brittle grass and the gaping cracks in the earth, and tried to picture parents and children stumbling across it. But they fit much better in the President's Wing, where golden dust motes are floating lazily through the brilliant stage lights, and Door C leads to Room 11, which looks exactly like Rooms 23, 13, and 35.

I was born in a workroom seven years ago.

Virginia is the only one who doesn't plan or rehearse. She doesn't share any of her memories, choosing instead to talk about her life today. She lives in the same compound as the rest of us, a dark hallway that is always perfectly still. She passes back and forth until she runs out of charge, day after day, like the rest of us, but still she says there are good times and bad. Her voice is clear and unashamed, and the things she says make me ache in my mechanical heart. Virginia is constantly being retuned, but eventually they'll realize the problem is that there isn't one. She just says what comes to mind.

She is honest as the sunrise. Her hands are small and delicate and her eyes never meet mine completely. I determinedly think of her as Virginia.

Once Virginia had a terrible malfunction. With

no warning at all, her eyes rolled back in their sockets and she crumpled to the floor, shaking like a leaf. We sent Taft to get help, but he's not exactly reliable, and I held her twitching body for nearly half an hour before anyone came. Sparks shot from her neck and her arms jerked up and down as if she were in pain, not that any of us can feel it. A useless cluster of presidents all shouted suggestions according to the medical knowledge of their day, but I couldn't calm her down or hold her still. Her head kept turning to the side again and again, and she looked for all the world like she wasn't even human. If she had tear ducts, she would have cried. When Andrew finally arrived, with Taft puffing and trailing behind, he dropped to his knees beside her and tore at her hair. I made a move to stop him, but the control panel emerging from behind her hair jarred me into immobility. I never felt that metal block in her skull when I ran my fingers through her hair.

Andrew deftly held her head still with one hand while pushing buttons with the other. Virginia went limp, and after a few more moments of frantic reprogramming Andrew sat back and sighed. Virginia twitched once, twice, and then lay still. She rose to her feet with many hard blinks and looked around nervously at our dumbstruck faces. "Hello?"

"Hello, Ms. Woolf," Andrew replied. "Welcome to the twenty-second century."

Aluminum bones can hold anything you put in them.

Underground, in a dark blue hall on a brilliantly lit stage, we talk all day and often into the night. We don't need to sleep, so we plug ourselves in and talk about our houses on Jackson Street, our wives, and our sons. Some of us outlived our children by centuries, while others are watching boys they never met grow up through headlines. I know their stories inside and out, but we need to tell them again and again, continuously without end. Whether it's my programming or this tug in my chest, or even if one's the other, letting go of Mary Todd and Tad is impossible. I live in their words, their silence, their smells and gestures. It's funny, but I remember the feel of them best. It's almost more an urge to touch them than to see them.

I swear in the reliving I feel it all more acutely than before, even if I never have felt it before. There's no going back—time travels in one direction, but it's the wrong one. I wish we could go backwards rather than forwards. I want to start with a mindful of memories, and know already which moments must be savored. I want to lose them when I reach them, unmake them, so I don't have to miss what I don't have. I want to end my life with a blank mind.

I dream of telling them so, but instead when I open my mouth only one thing comes out.

"On February 12, 1809."

||

THE SCENT OF IT

By Kayleigh Norgord
2015 Winner of the Henry Douglas Mackaman
Creative Writing Prize

The summer I turned sixteen was the summer my mother developed a gray streak of hair at the crown of her head. A single stripe of white emerged from her otherwise brown, shoulder-length bob in a matter of weeks, and it wasn't until the fog of summer had lifted and school began again that I finally noticed. I imagine her problems began early in June, shortly after my older sister, Angie, had returned home from college and after I learned of the affair.

I was painting my toenails on the front porch one afternoon while Angie was lying on the front lawn, smoking a cigarette and sunning herself with the strings of her suit untied, despite our neighbor's petulant phone calls. Our house was one of many primary-colored box houses with cutout shutters that never closed, on a street named after a tree. The yards contained pointed rose bushes in front of the porches, and the garages held at least two cars, plus one in the driveway if there were teenagers involved. The neighbor woman, Mrs. Peterson, had three teenage boys, and she told our mother that none of them needed to see my sister fixed across the lawn half naked.

As I sat on the porch I could hear my mother moving around inside the kitchen, and after a few moments she came spinning out of the house wearing a frown. Angie sighed and slapped a hand against her loose strings.

"She called," my mother said, skirting around the flower bed and standing over my sister on the lawn. It was odd seeing my mother's bare feet out in the open like that, white like two slabs of floured dough. She never left the house without shoes, even though it was 1970 and people were doing a great deal of stranger things.

"You think she would have some class," Angie said from behind her sunglasses. I watched the smoke lifting out of her mouth, snaking upwards in a sinister way like a cat's tail. Since returning home from school my sister had been smoking her head off and reading political books that upset my father a great deal. I was unsure what to make of it all: I had never read any controversial books and would not even know where to find some.

"She hung up when I answered," my mother said, staring over the brick house across the street. "But I knew it was her, I just have a feeling."

That's the moment I realized they weren't talking about Mrs. Peterson calling to complain again. They seemed to be talking about something else altogether.

My mother stood there tugging at the teal scarf in her hair for a while. I watched the back of her blouse, staring between the jut of her shoulder blades and considering what other woman she might be talking about, before I heard the phone ring.

Seeing as my mother was lost somewhere in her own mind and my sister was too lazy to stand up from the bath towel, I eased my way inside on my heels and across the orange kitchen tile to answer it.

"Hello," I said.

It was Blaine Matherson calling to ask if I could come out that night. For the past month he had been calling every few evenings to talk about nothing in particular, and sometimes he would invite me to one of his baseball parties where I felt mostly uncomfortable.

"We'll do something different," he said to me. "No parties this time."

I said okay, and he told me to wear my white miniskirt, the one I did not like because I had to yank it down regularly. That boy was always giving me indirect compliments, and I ate them one after the other like gumballs. By the time I hung up the phone, I had forgotten all about my mother wringing her hands outside and standing barefoot on our lawn.

Later that evening, Angie came into my room as I was getting ready for the night, even though it was six o'clock and Blaine would not be by to pick me up until eight thirty. She sat on the edge of my bed and watched me put on dramatic eye shadow in the mirror.

"So much blue," she said. I told her that the color made my eyes pop, and then she said, "Our father is having an affair."

I was not used to this new intensity about her, the way her words could clip and slice through the air. I dropped my makeup, clapping it onto the vanity.

"I blame the power structures," she said. "It's all about the male ego."

I blinked at the mirror, not wanting to interrupt and tell her I did not know what power structures she was referring to. As far as I knew, the only power that my father held over my mother involved setting the credit card limits.

"Anyways," Angie continued, "affairs happen all the time after traumatic events. It's not uncommon."

The traumatic event had happened a year ago when my older brother Peter was labeled missing in action, when really he was missing somewhere in South Vietnam. Angie was very able to discuss the matter openly, but I had learned not to think too much about it to prevent my imagination from running wild. I did not want to think about his dead body being swallowed by jungles that weren't on a map, or worse, being speared to a tree alive with his own teeth strung around his neck. My sister placed a hand on my shoulder.

"It's really not uncommon," she said again.

Her words bounced off of me, onto the carpet like hairpins.

The news was not as big of a shock to me as it would have been to other girls with fat, balding fathers who grew more turtle-like with age. My father, on the other hand, had a strongly cut chin and crow's feet that gave him a look of perpetual good humor even when he was angry, in which cases he was not a yeller and remained eerily quiet. My father dressed in dark suits that complemented his hair, which had been a lovely shade of silver since he was thirty-five. He was the type of man who struck up conversations with strange people in public places like cereal aisles and car dealerships. He was a successful banker and a fabulous dancer, the man who waved with one hand while pushing the lawn mower with the other.

The thought of another woman being attracted to my father was about as surprising to me as my own knees.

"What does Mom think of this?" I asked, thinking this a mature response. I was not going to stand up and stamp my feet or go barreling down the steps to chew out my father, the man who still pulled me into his lap and tickled my ribs every once in a while. I was not going to lose my head.

Angie shrugged, her shoulders dancing up and down aggressively like waves. "Oh, you know Mom," she said. "She's old school, she's confined by marriage. She accepts it as a phase."

Before I could sort out my own thoughts on the confines of marriage, my mother came into my room with a basket of folded laundry. I stared out the window and tried not to look at her too hard, but then she asked me if I would come to the department store with her, so I had to stare at her sensible trousers, her peach blouse, her dark eyebrows plucked in a dramatic arch.

"Can't tonight," I said to her clip-on earrings. "I've got a date."

My mother smiled and nodded before walking out of my room and back downstairs, the fabric of her pants swishing like wind. I imagined the woman my father was sleeping with did not wear pants loose enough to swish, and when I mentioned this to Angie she flashed her teeth in a peculiar smile.

"Are you kidding?" she said. "That kind of a woman doesn't wear pants at all."

I often lived things out differently in my own mind. That way things like baking a soufflé or having an affair turned out much better than they did in real life, with conclusions always reading the way they were supposed to.

For example, when my family received the news about Peter going MIA, I spent a great deal of time lying face down beneath my bed, where it was very dark, which I appreciated. My mother and father would knock on the door, and when I did not answer they would stick their necks in the room before seeing nobody was there, and then they would close the door again while I listened to their sluggish footsteps fade away. At the time he was labeled MIA, Peter had already been gone and drafted for a year, so after a few weeks of lying facedown on the carpet, I finally decided to just keep pretending he was gone from home temporarily, that all was going as planned. I would imagine him trekking about the mountains with a large backpack, or strumming a guitar by the fire like the soldiers they showed on the news, or at least used to show before everybody found out about the blood and killing bit.

Eventually, it came rather easily to me, this living life in my own head. Eventually, I became quite good at it.

By the time Blaine Matherson picked me up for our date, I had already begun to change a few things. I chose not to think about my father engaging in relations with another woman, for example, because Angie had said it was a common thing for a man—specifically our father—to stray a bit. I also chose to believe the things she said, even if a number of things about her of late confused me and she no longer wore a bra.

I knew that a lot of other girls my age would have stayed home after finding out that their fathers were sleeping with other women, but I also had known for the past year that my situation could not be compared to that of other girls: it was like constructing a volcano for the science fair, versus constructing a real, explosive volcano. As time went on, I had learned to stop trying to explain this to others and just accept it as true.

When I got into Blaine's car, he was rolling up the sleeves of an expensive sweater and looking past me, at the front window of the house. I eased the door closed quietly and waited for him to say something. Through the front window, Angie was flipping channels on the television, her brow knit, her face concentrated.

"My mother said your sister's on the pill," Blaine finally said.

We sat together and observed Angie curiously through the glass like a chimpanzee. When I did not respond he continued.

"You know what that means," he said.

Mrs. Matherson worked at the drugstore, filling people's prescriptions behind a large grey counter with a large gray sign boasting customer confidentiality. When I asked Blaine if his mother happened to read this sign, he looked very puzzled.

"Of course my mother can read," he said, pulling out of the driveway. "What does that have to do with anything?"

I decided to smile at him in response because I was convinced to have a good time. I crossed one leg over the other and sat up tall against the leather seat, listening to the radio. We drove in silence for a while, which did not bother me because I did not want him saying any more stupid things and ruining our date.

When Blaine first started hanging around my locker at the end of the school year, I thought it was because of Christopher Hartman, who was also a senior on the baseball team and whose locker was right next to mine. They would stand there talking about college ball and prom court, wearing the same kinds of button-down shirts with the same feathered hairstyles, and the whole thing started to annoy me greatly as I was always having to squeeze behind them to get to my locker. Then one day Christopher walked down the hall to class and Blaine just stood there, leaning against the lockers, not saying anything. I finally humored him and looked over my left shoulder, glancing at his Adam's apple, unable to look him fully in the eye. He asked what my name was and so I told him. Then he asked if I had ever been to a party, and I said I went to lots of parties. He laughed at that.

"I mean parties," he said, rounding his fingers around an imaginary can and tilting his chin, pretending to drink what I gathered was beer. I raised my eyebrows in response, and when I turned to leave he asked for my phone number. I gave it to him, despite his blonde feathered hair.

For the next week he called every few nights after seven o'clock to tell me about baseball practice, and even though I found the topic rather boring I pretended to be captivated. I would listen attentively, commenting here and there and waiting patiently for him to slip in the compliments.

"Sweaters look nice on you," he would say, or "Your eyes are kind of strange."

I was confused by that one. I had blue eyes and dark brown hair that people always mistook for black, just like the rest of my family with the exception of my father. As far as I knew, we all looked fairly normal.

"They're kind of mysterious, the way they linger," he said. "It works though."

When I hung up I considered how I would have reacted if it didn't work.

We drove along in Mr. Matherson's car for a while, continuing past our high school and some restaurants and the new strip mall that was just being put in. We kept on driving right out of the downtown area, into the country where Blaine finally swung the car into an empty church parking lot.

I assumed we were turning around and heading back into town, until he pulled into one of the spots and put the car in park. All around us it was dark and quiet, and the church stood glowing like the milky bones of a skeleton over in the corner of the lot. I looked over at Blaine and he turned the engine off before turning to look at me, reaching for my hand and smiling at me. I smiled back out of politeness.

Suddenly it all felt strange to me, like we were upside down or the car had lost its wheels.

"So where are we going?" I asked, working to hold my voice steady.

"I thought we'd stay here for now," he said.

When he leaned in I sat very still, my body cold, limp like a vegetable. I counted the seconds in my head and felt nothing, not saying a peep and hardly breathing. He kissed me. He tasted of meatloaf. I imagined his mother had cooked a lovely dinner of baked potatoes and cooked peas earlier that night, hurrying home from the pharmacy all frantic to prepare a meal and reapply her makeup before Mr. Matherson arrived home. For some reason the whole idea seemed ridiculous to me, and right then I started to laugh.

After a few moments Blaine pulled back and looked at me. The corners of his mouth turned up a bit in an amused way, but his eyes searched my face unevenly and I knew he felt very lost by my behavior. I watched him watching me, disorientated and panicked, and I laughed some more, wondering about the other girls who had sat in this passenger seat and how none of them had reacted this way when he kissed them. I laughed because I realized he had no idea what to do with me, that his time spent with more mature, experienced women and his narrow-minded mother had not prepared him in any way for this.

Despite his cluelessness, Blaine was a determined individual.

He sat there for another moment, blond eyebrows drawn together in what was clearly bewilderment, before he leaned back in and went on kissing my neck. Eventually I calmed down and the car was quiet again. Every once in a while he would say something nice about my hair or perfume, until eventually I stopped paying attention to what was happening in between the compliments. I imagined floating outside of myself, passing through the car window and up toward the treetops where I could build a bed of leaves still soft from the spring, where I could sleep for years. When I finally woke, I thought, maybe the affair would be over, and I could pretend it had all happened in a sick sort of dream.

After that I thought of my sister, bored out of her mind at home, speaking with urgency into the phone to someone I didn't know. Of my mother baking lemon bread in the oven. I imagined my father, seated on a floral couch in an apartment just far enough away, decorated with pastels and lace tablecloths like the pages of a magazine. I imagined a blond woman sitting next to him in a tight skirt and suit jacket, sipping tea from a dainty cup in a pronounced way with red fingernails.

That was as far as I could let myself think, and by the time I came to, I sensed that time had passed and my name had been repeated multiple times.

"Lucy," Blaine said. I opened my eyes.

I was situated in his lap, pressed between him and the steering wheel. There was a draft on my thighs and I noticed my skirt was bunched around my ribcage. My skin felt tight across the bones of my face. I realized I was crying.

"Oh," I said. I wiped my cheeks.

His eyes regarded me like two glowing dinner plates, shining empty through the darkness as I pulled my skirt back to its proper place. I crawled over to the passenger seat and asked to be taken home. Then I put on my seat belt and sat stiff, toes clenched inside of my shining, black leather shoes. Finally, he started the car and drove us both back into town without another word.

When we pulled into my driveway, I knew I had to address Blaine and perhaps even apologize for crying the way I had. I knew boys hated it when girls behaved unexpectedly like that, like I had twice that night—it made them shifty.

"I am not a crier," I heard myself saying. "I don't know where that came from."

This was a lie: I had a pretty good idea.

I turned and stared into his large, dumb eyes for a long time, waiting to see warmth and understanding or feel something violent, like an axe chopping into my stomach. All I saw was distress and baseballs.

"It's cool," Blaine said, an answer that left me feeling both relieved and unsatisfied. He relaxed. It occurred to me that the only thing I had in common with him at this particular moment was that we both knew my sister was on the pill, and we both had made out in a church parking lot. I suddenly felt let down.

"Well, thanks," I said.

It seemed like the appropriate thing to say after spending a strange night together.

Blaine nodded, confident once more and saying he would call after the game the next day. With nothing left to say, I kissed him good-night and stepped out of the car.

When I entered the house, I noticed something had changed. All of the lights were shut off and there were shadows littered in the hallway like black construction paper, but these things were not unusual as it was past ten o'clock and everyone was asleep, except for maybe Angie, who might be reading furiously in her bedroom. All of the frames on our wall were still perfectly aligned, and the only sounds to be heard were the dog barking down the block and the hum of the refrigerator. I sat down on the couch to think, staring at the television antennas and trying to identify what was different.

When it hit, it hit me square in the nose. Fruity

and strong as rubbing alcohol, I knew right away without having to ponder any longer.

There was a smell in my house.

Barely detectable beneath the scent other people noticed when they walked in the door, the smell of
wood and casseroles and clean, healthy people, was the
faint presence of a very strong perfume, the kind that
came from a department store and the kind my mother
would never wear. Right away I could tell it was not a
cheap perfume, but it was flowery and powerful even
in its diminished state. The kind of perfume that could
cause quite a few headaches. If the smell were a food,
it would have been a rotting banana contaminating
everything else in the refrigerator. If it came in a bottle,
the bottle would be made of indestructible plastic.

I sat on the couch and sniffed for a while.

After a few whiffs, it was gone, leaving me very
lightheaded and confused as to where it went. I lifted
the throw pillows one by one, inspecting their sharp,
square outlines and plunging my face deep into the
fabric. Then I gave up and walked upstairs to my room,
where I climbed into bed without bothering to change
into my pajamas.

I laid there in my now crumpled, white skirt,
listening to the sounds of nobody. Not smelling anything. I thought about Blaine's mother working all day
in the pharmacy and wondered who was to say that Mr.
Matherson wasn't seeing a special someone on the side
without her knowledge. This idea amused me and I
smiled to myself in the darkness. Mrs. Matherson was a
very tiny woman with short, permed hair and fluttering
eyes full of judgment, and I just knew an affair would
put her over the edge. She would probably lose it one
day at the pharmacy and mess up someone's prescrip-
tion, and then there would be lawsuits and maybe then
she would quit yapping about other people's medica-
tions. Quite possibly she would go completely mad and
start popping the pills like Tic Tacs, laughing wildly at
the ding of the cash register, before being placed in a
mental hospital by Mr. Matherson himself. Then she
would no longer wear a sick little smug smile while
gossiping with other fluff mothers at PTA meetings. I
made a mental note to mention this to someone other
than Blaine.

I rolled over and stared at the lines of light on my wall coming from the streetlamps outside and casting pale zigzags. I said a few words to God because that's what other Catholics like my mother had raised me to do in these situations. Talking to God works best if there are lists involved, so I listed off that I was thankful for an organized mother who enjoyed spending time with me, and for a handsome boy like Blaine with a bright, athletic future. Then I listed off the worries I had, that I hoped my brother was alive and my sister wasn't insane, before I addressed the bigger issue at hand. I told him I was willing to forget the whole affair business if my father ended it soon and so long as nobody mentioned it until many years had passed and our family could look back and laugh about it like an ugly school photo.

I was never sure if telling God my problems would make them vanish altogether, but it was nice to think I had some chance at reaching a better outcome in the end, whenever the end actually came. Without that, I knew I was hopeless.

After all was said, I closed my eyes, tired of staring at the optimistic white of the ceiling. I tried to think of nothing but the blackness that filled my room, and I imagined my voice sounding very puny and nasally to God, coming from a warm bed in a box house in a nice neighborhood, and meanwhile, there was a war going on across the ocean. I imagined he had voices chatting at him from all over the world about issues much greater than mine, but in the silence of my room, listening to the drum of my own restless heart, I refused to be ignored.

This is why I told God I would remain a mostly happy virgin until marriage if my family could go back to normal.

I had learned months ago that people often can't have the things they want, and although I did not want sex at that particular moment I figured I would want it sometime in the near future, which made it very valuable and perfect for bargaining. Another thing I knew about wanting things, was that a period of waiting was inevitable. This was not news to me. I knew that when I woke each morning—when I ate and dressed and read magazines in the sun—I was not fully a part of the life I was leading, the people I was speaking to or walking beside or going out on dates with. I was only waiting for this chapter of my life to end and be marked as "Tough Times" or "The Lost Year," so that I could go about my days without feeling as though my insides had been scooped out with a cold, metal spoon.

So I laid there, eyes closed, feeling swallowed by the dark. I was not worried or scared or even tired yet, because nothing about this idea of waiting surprised me anymore. I knew that I was only passing the time these days. I was always stuck in limbo, even when I was sleeping.

Even when I was pretending to feel fifteen.

||

To donate to the Henry Douglas Mackaman Creative Writing Prize, go to the University of Wisconsin Foundation page (www.supportuw.org) and click on "Give Online," which will take you to the "Make a Gift" page; then enter the "Henry Douglas Mackaman Undergraduate Writers Prize."

"

Before we go back to the music,
I want to point out something very
important. So I was in a bathroom,
and I will not say which bathroom,
but I saw the most excellent piece of
bathroom graffiti I've seen in a while.
It was written, etched into the wall:

I was stabbed on Mifflin and all I got was a lousy t-shirt.
Fantastic! How do you come up with that stuff? I was flabbergasted. I was filled with laughter, so much laughter. Although, getting stabbed isn't really funny, is it?

Henry,
The Grooving Tree
May 3, 2011

HOW I GOT MY SENSES

When the dull knife of introversion

had ceased its slow slice through stale friendships and social standings, Ray Davis found himself alone. Solitude was no stranger to him, but how strange it was that the faint pangs of loneliness should evaporate from his gut altogether. There was no bliss in the seclusion, and no joy in the damp basement where spiders spun translucent snares above the desk where he worked.

The occupant of this humble environment did not seek the praise of peers. He brought the stuff of his inner workings into the material world out of the necessity of pursuing a sense of self-worth and simple satisfactions. Ray considered his tasks noble in this way, but now he stared at the suspended magazine cutouts of Elliott Smith and Jeff Magnum, wondering if his time spent on similar endeavors was worth the empty feeling. He had been so sure of himself, but uneasiness rocked his once-steady mind. Maybe it was worth having friends for friendship's sake. He placed the old Martin guitar in its case, turned off the lights, and went upstairs.

Ray's father was in the process of hanging a string of jack-o'-lantern lights along the perimeter of the living room ceiling when his son emerged through the basement door. Edward Davis's slender frame teetered on the ladder as he struggled to fix the illuminated plastic pumpkins in place. Ray approached his father undetected—the sound of Bob Dylan's *Blonde on Blonde* masked his footsteps. The record was one of Edward's favorites and remained in consistent rotation on the family record player.

"But I would not feel so all alone . . . ," sang Edward as he precariously extended his reach toward the corner of the room.

"Everybody must get stoned!" sang father and son in unison as the former toppled to the ground. The record skipped on impact to "Pledging My Time."

"Jesus, Ray!" Edward said with a grin, rubbing his

hurting hip.

Most sixteen-year-olds choose to rebel against authority, but Ray liked his father, and had nothing to rebel against in this regard. The two were similar in sentiment, and although they routinely got lost in their respective worlds, an unspoken understanding held their planets together in orbit.

"Need any help?" Ray offered as his father stood up.

"Bob and I have this under control," he said, picking up the pumpkins. "But why don't you go out back and bring your Grandpa some lasagna? I'm sure he's hungry by now. He forgets to eat."

"Sure thing," Ray replied as he turned to go.

"And don't forget to bring in the rent," Edward said with a wink and a grin. Ray rolled his eyes and went into the kitchen.

Ray's grandfather could have had the guest room, but chose instead to live in the tree house in the backyard. Edward and Ray had built the structure together long ago, but it was Nolan Davis who had claimed it as his own. The seventy-year-old was nimble, and enjoyed climbing the wooden ladder up the old oak tree to his elevated dwelling. Nolan attributed his agility to his time in Vietnam—"The government turned me into a jungle cat; that's how I got my senses," he would say. Ray wanted to like his Grandpa, but Nolan had shut himself in the tree with his poetry and his pot, and he shot in and out of the lives of his offspring like a comet.

Ray brought the cold lasagna to the base of the oak tree and could smell the skunky smoke above him. He could hear the muffled sound of The Doors' first record winding to an end, as Jim Morrison crooned, *"All the children are insane . . ."*

"Hey, Grandpa, I brought dinner!" Ray shouted, arching his neck upwards.

The music swelled as the wooden panel above the ladder slid open, and Nolan peered down. His wavy white locks made his silhouette haggard, like a stoned Einstein. He repositioned the wooden panel and sent down a bucket attached to a rope. Ray put the plate in the bucket and watched as it returned into the darkness. Ray sighed and remained rooted at the base of the tree.

"Hey, Grandpa!" Ray shouted.

The wooden panel shot out of position and Nolan appeared once more as Jim Morrison continued, *"There's danger on the edge of town . . ."*

"Rent!" Ray yelled. Nolan stared at his grandson for a few seconds and moved away from the hatch, leaving it open. Ray took the invitation and climbed up the tree into Nolan's lair, but he felt uneasy doing so.

The room reeked of weed—the two-by-fours that made up the walls would not let go of the smoke they had captured. The room was only big enough for a mattress, a desk, a record player, and a few plants of a certain demeanor—but Nolan had simple needs. War souvenirs covered every inch of wall space, save for the window, and a dusty carpet covered Edward's amateur flooring job. The entire room slanted considerably. Nolan sat on his mattress with the lasagna and watched as his grandson returned the carpet to completion by restoring the wooden panel to its rightful place.

"You're here for the rent, but my money's all spent. So, for the protector of my genes, I offer a different kind of green," said Nolan in a raspy voice as he motioned toward the jars on his desk.

"Dad wouldn't have it any other way," Ray replied. He remembered how much he liked the way his grandpa spoke.

"What's Eddy listening to these days? I've got a sweet strain of Jimi's signature Purple Haze, or how about I throw some groovy Albert Green your way?" Nolan pointed to the different jars as he spoke.

"Still Bob Dylan, as always."

"Ah, I've got just the thing for that folky tone." He grabbed a jar from his desk and smelled the contents. "Here's a new batch of Rolling Stoned." He pulled a baggie from his pocket and shook enough from the jar to fill it halfway up. He handed the bag to Ray, and the two exchanged a nod. Ray turned toward the hatch.

"Any plans for this night of fright?" asked Nolan,

his mouth half-full of lasagna.

"Not really."

"You and your friends aren't making any mischief?"

Ray gave a wry smile and opened the hatch.

He climbed down the ladder and paused on his way to the back door to look at the moon. He thought about how it looked to the world outside of Richmond, Indiana, and how strange it was to be such a solitary figure so small in the grand scheme of the universe. Edward had finished decorating the house by the time Ray returned. Halloween was Edward's favorite holiday, and he insisted on completing his annual rituals with care. The pumpkins had been carved several days before, and they flickered on the front steps. Ray had grown out of the youthful giddiness of the holiday several years ago, but he pretended to feel the same things his father did. After all, wasn't that the point— pretending?

"How's Nolan?" asked Edward, who was now dressed as Superman.

"Same as always." Ray handed his father the baggie.

"Did he give you a hard time?" Superman sniffed the pot.

"No, but I don't like it up there."

"Nolan is the only one who does. Now go and get your costume on—the trick-or-treaters will be here soon." Edward produced rolling papers from the kitchen cabinet drawer and started an instinctive process.

Ray wasn't allowed to smoke until he finished school, but he didn't mind. Pot didn't appeal to him, but he saw no harm in it. Even if it was a bad thing, how could he blame his father? He understood that everyone copes with loss differently, and to each his own.

"I'm going to go play guitar for a while," said Ray, and he pretended not to see the disappointment in his father's face as he turned toward the basement.

"To each his own," mumbled Edward as he licked the gum of the bulging paper and rolled it into a cone.

Ray entered the basement and plucked the old Martin guitar from its case. His dad had given it to him when he turned thirteen, but he looked at it not as a gift, but as the six-stringed form of a life insurance check. Ray didn't resent the instrument—he was simply aware of its origins, and origins can't be helped. He tuned it up and strummed an E minor to double check. E was Ray's reference pitch, but it was never major. The guitar shook with another forceful E minor, but Ray wasn't worried about volume. Edward had soundproofed the basement, so nothing could come in or out. Ray began the intro to "These Days" by Nico—he liked her work much more after she left the Velvet Underground.

"I've been out walking. I don't do too much talking these days . . ."

Ray felt a warmth grow inside his chest as his fingertips carefully plucked the notes within the chords.

"These days I seem to think a lot about the things that I forgot to do."

His voice couldn't hold a pitch the way his fingers could, but then again, neither could Nico, and she couldn't even play guitar.

"And all the times I had the chance to . . ."

He let the final chord of the phrase ring out and turned to his desk. It was littered with crumpled pieces of paper, dirty dishware, and some texts by the likes of Heidegger and Sartre that he didn't understand. Ray was aware of how much he had yet to learn, and this excited and frightened him at the same time. His brain would connect and decipher the future events of his life through the lens of the experiences that would ultimately define his character—this, he thought he was sure of. Music made sense in this way—he would send his experiences through the processing plant of his fingers, and thus capture the ever-changing lens of his perception at one point in time. Ray then considered that these thoughts might be useless if he didn't have anyone to share them with. Ray looked at his picture of Elliott Smith and felt the pangs of loneliness return as his father lit up in the backyard. Neither Davis knew that the spiders were watching.

The doorbell rang, and Edward stomped out his joint and raced inside. He grabbed the bowl of candy from the kitchen and opened the basement door.

"C'mon, Ray, it's show time!"

Ray put the guitar back in its case and begrudgingly walked up the stairs. Edward had already opened the front door by the time Ray made it to the living room. Edward did not greet the doorbell ringers as Ray had expected.

"Where are your costumes?" asked an offended Edward.

"We're on our way to get them," came a voice from the doorway. "We saw your lights were on."

Ray walked to his father's side and saw three men standing in the doorway. He recognized one of them from his high school, but he was one grade above him at least—maybe even a senior. The other two seemed older. One had sideburns that covered the majority of his cheeks, and the other had severe five-o'clock shadow.

"Are you Ray's friends?" Edward asked, eagerly looking to his son. Edward had always wanted Ray to have friends.

"We've seen each other around," said the boy Ray recognized. "My name's Stevie."

The boy outstretched his hand, and Ray shook it tentatively. Edward smiled.

"I'm Ray."

"Nice to meet you, Ray," said Stevie.

"What are you up to tonight?" asked the man with sideburns.

"Just playing guitar in the basement, I guess."

"You play guitar? Are you any good?" asked Stevie.

"Not really—I'm still learning."

"Mind if we hear a sample?" said the man with sideburns. The man with whiskers stood silently, fidgeting.

"Why don't you show them your stuff?" said Edward, smiling at his son.

Ray shrugged his shoulders and led the men to

the basement. The man with sideburns shut the door as the group descended into the dark. Ray turned on the light and grabbed his guitar. The men stood over him as he played an E minor.

"You smoke dope?" said the man with sideburns.

"No."

"Bullshit."

"No, I really don't."

"We saw you," said the man with whiskers.

"We smelled you," said the man with the sideburns.

"I don't smoke; my dad does," Ray replied. In the light of the basement, he saw the whiskered man's glossy eyes. He noticed that all three had the same eyes—red, darting.

"So, he's holding?" asked the man with the sideburns. He looked at the man with whiskers and smiled.

"Well—" Ray was cut off.

"Never mind," said the man with sideburns. "We're going to use the bathroom."

Ray wanted to say something—he was confused.

"Play me a song," said Stevie as his companions went upstairs.

"What was that about?"

"Nothing, everything is crystal perfect," he said with a smile. "Now play me a song." Stevie sat on the stairs.

Ray felt strange, so he started to play.

After the first few chords of Elliot Smith's "Needle in the Hay," the two men saw what they were looking for.

"Your hand on his arm, the haystack charm around your neck."

The two men found Edward sitting by the front door.

Ray's voice cracked through the verse, and his fingers trembled. Stevie stared into his eyes.

"Needle in the hay . . . Needle in the hay . . ."

Edward stood up, but the man with whiskers grabbed his shoulders and threw him down.

"Needle in the hay . . . Needle in the hay . . ."

Ray's voice was shaking, and Stevie smiled, revealing all his awful teeth.

"He's wearing your clothes, head down to toes, a reaction to you."

The man with sideburns was screaming into

Edward's ear.

"You say you know what you did, but you idiot kid, you don't have a clue."

Edward didn't want to say anything, but the man with sideburns took out a knife from his boot.

"Sometimes they just get caught in the eye."

Ray felt a sharp pain in his chest as Stevie laughed.

"Needle in the hay . . . Needle in the hay . . ."

The men carried Edward to the backyard.

Stevie laughed uncontrollably. Guitar in hand, Ray saw his moment and rushed past Stevie up the stairs. He saw that there was no one in the house, and that the back door was open. Candy was scattered across the floor. Ray ran through the door in time to see the man with whiskers climbing the oak tree. Jimi Hendrix's "All Along the Watchtower" was blaring from Nolan's lair. Ray ran toward the men with Stevie close behind. He gripped the guitar so tightly that his knuckles went white. He saw his father on the ground, twitching at the base of the tree.

The man opened the hatch to the tree house and climbed through. There was shouting, then a crash, and the music stopped.

Silence, then a scream! The horrible sound filled the night, and both Ray and Stevie stopped in their tracks as the man with whiskers fell backwards through the window and out of the tree, landing on his head. Stevie and the man with sideburns took off running as Ray sprinted toward the man. Up close, Ray saw a Vietcong standard-issue field knife in the man's ribs.

"Mom . . . ," he mumbled. "Momma!" Ray stood over him, trembling.

"Momma," said Ray with quivering lips.
He looked at his father, and then at the man.

He raised the guitar over his head and smashed it into the man's mouth. The man screamed. Ray raised the ruined instrument and slammed it into the man's face again. The man was silent. Ray's movements were mechanical—over and over, an easy rhythm.

"Enough!" yelled Nolan as he climbed down the

tree. Ray dropped the guitar, turned to his father, and fell to his knees.

Edward was shaking, the red cape draped over his body. Nolan turned Edward on his back and stripped off the costume.

"It's gonna be all right," said Nolan as he stared into his son's eyes. "No major arteries. Ray!"

Ray regained composure and dialed 911, his fingers trembling. He looked back at the stiff body of the whiskered man.

"I want to die," Edward choked out.

"No you don't," said Nolan, moving his eyes to Ray, who only heard the dispatcher.

"Katie," he said.

"Ray," Nolan whispered as he grabbed his son's hand.

Ray ended the call and helped Nolan apply pressure to Edward's chest. The son tended to his father, and the father tended to his son. The Davis's planets were aligned.

Ray looked at the moon, understanding that he had never really been alone.

||

Nope, still warped. We can only do so much. See, that's part of the pleasures of owning vinyl.'

Slowly watching the music you love die.

Right. And contort. And melt. And . . . yeah. Because life is fragile. Like vinyl records. Right. We just spin around until we can't spin no more, and that's it for us.

And that's what this DJ has to say about that.

Henry and Max Fisher
on *Strange Groove,*
after attempting to play a warped
David Bowie record on air
September 26, 2012

HENRY AND GRAMMA'S

Henry & Gramma's
Magic

PANCAKES

Dedicated to my Grandma Cord you make my life a little bit sweeter.

MAGIC PANCAKES

By Henry Mackaman, age 9

"What a rotten day! Henry exclaimed. "It's too cold and rainy for me to play outside"

Henry walked down the street Granny's house. Granny was waiting for him at the door.

"Hello Henry!" said Granny, "How are you today?"

"Not good Granny, I can't play outside!"

"Well then come inside and Granny will make you some pancakes."

"Thanks, but no thanks" said Henry, "I'm too sad to eat pancakes"

"Nonsense!" said Granny, and the two went into the kitchen.

Granny's kitchen was bright and shiny. It's counters were filled with bowls and containers, filled with spices and sweets.

"Now you sit on this stool and I'll have some pancakes ready in no time!" Granny grabbed a bowl and threw a bunch of things in. After a blur of mixing and blending, Granny was done. She filled her wooden spoon

with the mixture and made circles on the scalding griddle. Soon enough pancakes were piled high before Henry.

"Gee thanks Granny, but I don't see how pancakes could cheer me up!"

"Scientists have proven that indulging in sweets is not an effective method for subsiding a sadness but rather an immature alternative for short term relief, not to mention the health violations that could danger my dietary values. I'll be six soon Granny! I've got to watch my health!"

"Just try one bite" said Granny.

"What do you put into these pancakes Grandma?" yelled Henry, "These pancakes are unbelievable!"
"Well," said Granny, There are a couple ingredients.* Milk, water, bisquick and my secret ingredient."

"Well," said Henry. "Well," said Granny, "What is your Secret?" Henry asked. "If I told you," Grandma explained, "it wouldn't be a secret!"

"Pleese tell!" begged Henry. "Okay" said Granny, "Its just a little bit of love!"

"What? That was it? That was your big finish? Love? Hah! Such absurdities will not fool my advanced brain!" said Henry.
"No not real love," said Granny, "no, the new "love" sugar from Betty Cracker*!"

"Really?"

"No, I mean "love", the new buttermilk from Land o Lakes"

"You are really gullible!" said Granny. "Man I had you going!"

"Really?"

"ARE YOU KIDDING?"

"I can't believe it?" said Granny, "and the school says you are a genius superstar who will live to be the greatest person to ever live? (Besides Micheal Jordan of course.)"

"Point blank," said Granny, "If you are ever mad or sad, you can always come to Granny. Or if Granny can't cheer you up, Granny's super magical pancakes will, made with new "love" b'squick.

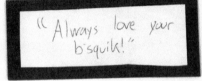

"Always love your b'squik!"

"Really?"

"Happy Birthday Grandma!"

Love - Henry

LYON HEART

HENRY VILAS ZOO

Henry Mackaman Memorial Bench on the Mississippi River

"The truth of the matter is so many friends and family members miss Henry Mackaman. He was a talented writer and musician, but most importantly he was a generous, kind, and sweet young man. The Mississippi River begins in Minnesota where Henry lived most of his short life and winds through Mississippi where he spent his early childhood years. We are raising money to install a memorial bench along the bluffs in Saint Paul so that Henry's friends and family can sit, write and remember him."

—Lisa Heyman

After fifty-one donors raised over $3,500, Henry's bench and plaque were installed on October 15, 2014 on the Mississippi River Road walking path between South Woodlawn Avenue and Highland Parkway in Saint Paul, MN. His bench faces north with a view of the Mississippi River and in the distance, the city of Minneapolis.

Henry Mackaman Memorial Bench at the Henry Vilas Zoo

"It was just a couple of months after my Henry died, when I learned that Henry the lion at the zoo in Madison had died.

I was struck by the coincidence.

So I wrote to the zoo and sent a donation along with a drawing that Margaret Palmquist had done of the two Henrys.

They replied with a sweet letter and a stuffed animal lion for me.

So I started investigating how I could memorialize my Henry at the zoo. I saved my pennies and decided on a bench. Margaret chose a spot right in front of the lions' den. Perfect.

Long after the bench was placed, I discovered that The Henry Vilas Zoo was in memory of another Henry, who at the age of twenty-one died from complications of diabetes.

Another coincidence?

You tell me."

—Meredith Leigh, Henry's mom

NO LIGHT

Late at night, when there's nowhere left to go, we go to the St. Thomas campus. There is a bench there that looks out over the Mississippi River, but it's hard to see once Walter has set up his hookah and the smoke has drowned out everything.

The guards come every once in a while, but they're in their twenties and often take drags from the green velvet hoses. We smoke weed once we know the guards have left, not because we think they'll bust us, but because we don't want to share.

Walt and I are just about done setting up the hookah when Gunnar's Volvo pulls up next to the curb. He's dressed in black, and as he takes a cigarette from his shirt pocket I say to Walter that he looks like a priest. Gunnar works at a classy restaurant in the neighborhood with the biggest houses, and sometimes he sneaks bottles from the wine cellar, but tonight he is empty handed.

"Ugh. You wouldn't believe the night I had," he says, walking up the hill to our bench. Walter breaks apart a coal and places it on top of the hookah.

"Cal Ripken Jr. came into Frost's tonight—he reserved a table for fifteen!"

"You must've got a hell of a tip!" I say while picking up a hose and plugging the end. Walter gives me a nod and sucks his hose.

"Fuck no. The prick stiffed us!" He pulls out an empty pocket from his slacks.

"I thought Cal was the Iron Man! He's the most dependable player in baseball."

Gunnar takes a seat at the table and smiles. He reaches into his other pocket and pulls out a bulging baggie.

"For the record, the man is a very generous tipper. In fact, Cal Ripken is the reason why we'll be rippin'."

Walter turns to him and releases a cloud of smoke into his face. I laugh, but Gunnar isn't amused.

"What the fuck, man! You always do this."

Walter smiles, and the sound of the bubbling hookah fills the silence of the night.

Gunnar grabs the hose from Walter's hands and the hookah crashes to the ground. The burning coals are dancing at our feet.

Walter stands up. The hookah is cracked beyond reasonable repair. He stares at Gunnar, and walks away. I know Gunnar feels like a jerk, but he won't show it.

"What's his problem?" he says, still holding the useless velvet hose.

"Let's go," I say. Gunnar looks at me as if to say "Where?"

"Anywhere."

We get inside the Volvo, and Gunnar turns the key in the ignition without a word. The radio comes to life at full blast—Arcade Fire's "Une Annee Sans Lumiere." The jangly guitar begins as Gunnar puts the car in drive, and the drums kick in as he steps on the gas pedal. Gunnar doesn't speak French and can't understand most of the lyrics like I can. He also doesn't know what happened to Walter's dad, but then again, neither do I.

||

"

I think Paul Simon just
put out a new album.
You know what, he
always wears a hat
now. He won't take his
hat off.

He's just continuously making comeback albums. Every album is his next *Graceland.*

"This is the one. I can feel it. If I just keep this hat on, and I keep my fingers crossed . . . "

Henry and Max Fisher,
The Grooving Tree
September 26, 2012

HAZE

We spend our days in
Medicinal hazes
Opening gates inwards
New fields to graze in
This colorful consciousness grows
Lost in the ebb and flow
For all we know
The bright lights will never show
Upon a meaning or motive to be
So let this haze lull me to sleep
We'll try to set a tortured mind at ease
Redefined responsibilities
If at least finding inner peace
Praying to make believe
Until the sun sets at last
On future, present, and past
For all we know
The bright lights will never show
Upon a meaning or motive to be
So let this haze lull me to sleep

THE FOREST FESTIVAL

The concrete's a rough blooded barrenscape
Crafted of unconscious convolution
You'll do well to escape to a foreign place
The forest festival
We'll wait for ya there
This forest has come alive
Come for the luminate spectacle
Stay for the tales of a time forgotten
Safe haven to hide from a hectic world
Follow your senses, they'll take ya there
I cannot consciously contemplate what I am feeling
Shooting sensations in starlight is soul healing
I cannot recall a single word
My mother moon I follow
This forest festival
Out in the hollow
The glare of father son I follow
This forest festival
Out in the hollow

A LETTER FROM ANDREW

I first met Henry during the summer when he and Owen would come to England during the British Studies Program. Henry, being Henry, was always friendly, polite, and happy, and I was always interested in the shows and museums he and Owen were going to see—in the early days with Doug or some other adult, and later by themselves, with a great air of independence and self-reliance.

Being one adult among many that Henry was meeting, I hadn't thought that I'd made much impression until one evening, during the class research forum, I looked up into the high balcony to see Henry and Owen sitting by themselves. Henry waved to me. It was just a slight, friendly wave, accompanied by Henry's clever and slightly ironic smile, to acknowledge that we had seen each other across all the noise and nerves.

When I discovered that Henry was enrolling in the inaugural Compass program last summer, I wrote Doug and told him that the news had made my day. In a class of high achievers and distinctive and creative students, Henry thrived and enjoyed every day of lectures, visits to museums, galleries, and historical sites, and evenings of wandering to parks and cafés and public spaces. Henry had those qualities that I consider important in any student, but absolute in friends: intelligence, honesty, and generosity. I suppose all teachers since Socrates have wanted students who follow their ideas and become disciples, but the truly great teachers, like Socrates, wish for the alchemy of education to happen: that unexplainable magic that turns readers into greater translators of Old English than the master, researchers into finders of new scientific connections, and observers into discoverers of new relations between artists and their abilities to turn materials into psychological insight.

This transformation happened to Henry during the Compass course. I am not so arrogant as to believe that this happened because of me. In fact, in several of the literary works we read for the summer, there are cautionary tales about teachers, and while I don't believe myself so bound in theory like Dr. Pangloss that I don't see the contrary evidence standing before me in the embodiment of Candide, nor do I want to be like Aschenbach, the German writer in Thomas Mann's *Death in Venice,* who, inspired to artistic raptures by the beauty of young Tadzio, remains what Henry called a "withered workaholic." Part of the explanation may be what happens to a number of students when they are engaged in international education: take bright and curious seekers, take them to a number of museums, galleries, and historical sites, make a few salient points, and let them go.

The group dynamic worked for Henry because Henry's generosity with his time and energy and empathy made him one of the favorites of the group. Often I would see Henry talking with different members of the class, moving from table to table at meals to be with people he didn't know as well or people who had not quite become integrated into the class.

Part of what happened to Henry during the Compass summer may be illustrated by a phrase from one of Henry's essays for the final examination. In an essay on the relation of the self to other people, Henry concludes, after discussing *Death in Venice* and *Survival in Auschwitz:* "Only in solitude can we truly be ourselves, but only in company can we become who we are." Henry wrote thoughtful and cogent responses to questions about the individual being: the pose of jaded rebel in Byron, the existential isolation of Meursault in *The Stranger,* the reduced self of Primo Levi in his days in Auschwitz. Perhaps Henry's greatest empathy came in his responses to the personal experiences of Maurice Cling in his recollections of his daily life in Auschwitz or to Cam Beech's account of warfare as we stood on the beach at Normandy. Henry was comfortable with his own solitude; his intelligence allowed him to be comfortable in his own skin, as the cliché goes; his intelligence allowed him to say, in response to Camus, "What good is the individual's existence and why try to understand it? Perhaps the answer is to ask more questions."

Perhaps as well as from his intelligence, Henry's self-reliance came from his understanding of words and their power and their limitation. Less effective are words trying to define or explain pain or suffering or the nature of existence. Perhaps this understanding led Henry to his great love of music and his growing appreciation of painting and sculpture. These art forms, with their appreciable lack of content, fascinated Henry. Henry's love of music I will leave for others to talk about; but music obviously touches emotions and feelings that words cannot explain. Henry understood music's role in those moments of solitude and pain, as he wrote in some song lyrics:

> So I played guitar all night long
> Until I broke a heart string
> Time will heal all of my wounds
> But it doesn't hurt to sing
> No, it doesn't hurt to sing.

What I can speak about is Henry's growing appreciation of painting and sculpture. Again, some of this is due to the nature of the Compass program. Take intelligent and thoughtful students and, in the course of five weeks, put them in the Rijksmuseum, the Van Gogh Museum, the Pergamon Museum, the Holocaust Memorial, the Musée D'Orsay, the Louvre, the National Portrait Gallery, the National Gallery, and the British Museum, and some aesthetic sense will probably develop. Yet for Henry, paintings and sculpture became more than color and line, space and shadow, composition and perspective. Art became that experience in which one feels with one's eyes.

At the end of the Compass program, Henry stayed a few days in London as did I, and we spent several days together exploring the National Gallery, the British Museum, and, perhaps most important for Henry, the Courtauld Collection. In that great collection of Impressionist and post-Impressionist paintings, Henry came to love one of my favorite paintings, Manet's *A Bar at the Folies-Bergère*.

The painting is in some ways what it calls itself: a painting of a barmaid, the bar laden with champagne bottles, a bowl of oranges, and some flowers, a gentleman talking to the barmaid, all reflected in a mirror behind. Yet, as one studies the painting, one realizes that the perspective is not quite right—the back of the barmaid talking to the customer is not a mirror image of the barmaid facing us; the bottles are not in the right position. Most enigmatic of all is the face of the barmaid looking out of the painting at us—tired, half-smiling, thoughtful, distant—the face raises as many questions as the intriguing smile of the Mona Lisa, perhaps more. What is she thinking about? The ambiguities and mysteries of the painting begin to intensify; the painting ceases to be about a story and more about the nature of modern life and the nature of modern art. Why did this painting appeal to Henry? Perhaps, as he said, it raises questions about the nature of existence, and as there are no simple answers, one can only ask more questions.

I have been speaking of the effect of the Compass program and our relationship in it on Henry. Let me conclude by speaking briefly about Henry's effect on me. Always there is the pleasure of sharing works of art and literature that you love with those who are eager to learn and come to appreciate them. As Henry said, we are most truly ourselves when we are alone, but we learn who we are through our relationships with others. I think more often and with deeper insight about Rembrandt and Manet and the Pergamon Altar because I talked about them with Henry. When I was at the Getty Museum last Christmas and saw Van Gogh's *Irises*, it brought back a wonderful day in Amsterdam at the Van Gogh Museum last summer, but it also brought back those moments in the Van Gogh Museum when I stood with Henry and talked about line and color, but more importantly, the loneliness of that bedroom with the single bed and single chair. Having known Henry and the effect of his eager seeking to learn and understand reminds me of the W.S. Merwin poem, "Separation":

> *Your absence has gone through me*
> *Like thread through a needle.*
> *Everything I do is stitched with its color.*

Thank you for this opportunity,
Andrew Woolley

A Bar at the Folies-Bergère by Édouard Manet.

JOURNALS: HENRY IN EUROPE

1: WELCOME TO THE WORLD

5/26/2012

After having spent many hours hovering over the Atlantic, I find myself standing on an Amsterdam street corner with three people I barely know. We are all a little dumbfounded; a red-faced Dutchman had just herded us off a tram, and suddenly, we are on our own. Needless to say, we have close to no idea where we are, but somehow I don't feel lost. For some reason, direction does not seem to be an issue, and this idea soon becomes a reoccurring theme when later traversing the whimsical one-ways dreamed up by cheeky Dutch city planners.

Still, the ebb and flow of Amsterdam is hazardous to sleep-deprived foreigners such as ourselves, and one comes to wonder whether the silent blinking tram beacon serves as a sufficient warning to their intermittent presence. Nevertheless, my merry men manage to make our way to the Stayokay hostel in minutes, and our first day in Amsterdam is only beginning.

I had no intention of waiting to explore the city, so Dan, Haley, and I make our way out into the streets. The commercial districts were a little overwhelming at first, and some streets feel more like an outdoor mall than anything else. Still, there is something unique about how the shops operate. It didn't take us long to see that the city is divided into sectors: the shoe sector, the pizza sector, the art sector, etc.

The shops strewn together are selling very similar things, and therefore create a nearly perfectly competitive market. Perhaps this is why eager patrons persistently talk up their shops when we walk by, and this phenomenon tried our tired travelers' minds. People with money are popular people.

Settling into the hostel is merely a break in the exploration, and Dan and I soon decide that another adventure is in order. Unfortunately, our wide-eyed wandering lands us in the middle of a foreign intersection as the temperature dips down to a chill, and ominous clouds feign rain. But panic is not to be grabbed with helpless hands, and we have a mutual confidence in our navigation know-how.

However, the city's eager serpent had offered us apples all night, and the ensuing confusion banished us from our familiar world. The key to our safe return came in the form of trams, or rather tram stops, which feature illuminated maps, which glowed a hopeful glow of help and understanding for our plight. Needless to say, we made it home safe as two humbled travelers, still kindling our adventure's fire with an explorer's optimism.

2: THE MOVING STILL LIFE

5/30/2012

Amsterdam has been kind to me, and I know that although I will be leaving soon, I will definitely be coming back. However, a large part of the love I have for this place is due to the people around me. I have made lifelong friends within four days, and there is something to be said for that.

I already feel that I have learned quite a bit on this adventure, and the lectures we've held in beautiful Vondelpark seem to seep into everyday life, holding a spooky relevance I didn't initially expect. Having a sense of Dutch history puts its architecture and art in context, and the perspective I've gained has heightened my appreciation and awareness for my surroundings.

Visiting the Dutch Resistance Museum put even more ideas in my head when I later wandered through the streets of Amsterdam. *My, how you've changed!* I think to myself, but then again, I am not just referring to the city. Jason and I talk about this concept in depth, and cite the proximity of Anne Frank's annex to the red-light district as a sign of the times. What if one could super-impose an image of this block seventy years ago over an image as we see the same spot today?

Although the landscape has changed with time, one may look through the ever-constant lens of a painting for a picture of the past, and Amsterdam is filled with such art. My time at the Rijksmuseum is spent trying to comprehend the context of the paintings I am seeing, and the artist's intent seems to hang in a fog of individual interpretation and perspective. *How meaning evolves with time!* I think, staring at a still life.

These scenes of a table's contents capture my attention like no other paintings. Different artists use the same subjects: a silver pitcher, a small green glass, an apple, a half-eaten roll, etc. I see how every object interacts and reflects each other—even the apple's subtle shine is evident in the contorted glimmer of light on the silver pitcher! Every object works together to create the big picture. This is how I feel about the group.

How can I talk about art without mentioning the Van Gogh Museum? It would be a crime to do so. I am a sponge soaking up the controlled chaos of an Impressionist, but a single sponge cannot hope to traverse the Titanic's deck! The liberal use of color— painting tree trunks purple, coloring in fields with pink! What a freedom it must be to know the rules only long enough to break them.

If a picture cannot do these paintings justice, then what good can words do? So, I will not describe the paintings, but rather my feelings. I am connected to the imperfect edges of Vincent's landscapes—more of a mood than an image. Power lies in connection, not detail, and what connections I have made in the past few days! I am no longer just a traveler, but a friend, a confidant, an energy, an explorer, and right now, tired.

Rest must be with us all so that tomorrow can glow as brilliantly as today.

3: OH, THE GERMANS...

6/2/2012

What a blur these traveling days have been! I am constantly lost — not in the sense of not knowing, but rather in the sense of exploring.

My group took a train from Amsterdam to Brussels, and arrived under the growing chance of rain. The sky was dark, but our eyes were bright, and with a traveler's courage we set off. It turned out that our hostel was at the very edge of the city, but a quick tram ride could take us within range. However, at this point we still don't know exactly where we are, so I decided to dust off my French and ask for directions. We wandered into a gas station, and I began to converse with the clerk. After some initial confusion, we communicated effectively, and my group began our hike to the hostel.

What should we see as we get closer to the hostel, but Haley, Kendle, Cara, Ray, and Brittany! Our groups combined, and we decided to head to the Grand Place for dinner, waffles, and beer. Finding food is not hard in Brussels, and soon we were being herded into a restaurant. After a pot of mussels, a plate of escargots, and a pint, a collective smile appeared. 'Twas a fantastic first night of independent travel!

Let me skip ahead to one of the most bizarre nights of my life, which happened to be the following evening. We checked into our hostel in Cologne, and Jason and I decided to do our laundry. The German Laundromat was confusing, to say the least, and we couldn't figure it out to save our lives. An elderly German woman began to take interest in us, and she was soon walking us through the process. She spoke with both her mouth and her hands, and we were able to understand enough to start our washing machines. However, in order to put Jason's clothes in, the woman took someone else's clothes out—and this person walked in shortly after the spin cycle began, and she was NOT happy. She began to glare at Jason, and refused to give up the gun. Her stare was so intense that we decided to leave the Laundromat, which inevitably led to finding a bar. Little did we know what we had in store.

We walked into a pub filled with the sound of a drunken German chorus, led by beer-fisted men with big smiles and small glasses. We were the youngest pub goers by twenty-five years, and the only non-locals. Although I can't speak any German, I was aware that the ensuing laughing was directed at us—the stares gave them away. However, one of the men turned to us and introduced himself as Christopher.

"Don't mind them, they're drunk," he said. "But so am I!" He then taught us how to order a beer—ein Kölsch! (Kölsch is the favorite beer in Cologne.) He told us how to say cheers (Prost!), and that one cannot drink until everyone has been served. "When all of our drinks arrive, we all say 'Prost!' and clink our beers."

Christopher became irate after we took our first sip, explaining that we were not clinking our glasses properly. "Clinking Kölsch is like being with a woman," he said while lifting his glass and angling toward his face, and he instructed us to do the same. "You must take her from behind!"

We laughed and clinked the bottom of our glasses. Soon the Germans were buying us drinks, and we were buying them drinks, and before I knew it, I was being taught how to conjugate the verb "to go" in German. As it turns out, almost every German verb is irregular, meaning that each pronoun has an individual conjugation for every verb!

All the while, we were running back and forth between the bar and the Laundromat checking on our clothes, which still came out damp after an outrageously long dryer cycle.

Perhaps it was fitting—some nights aren't meant to be dry.

4: THE WORDS OF FATHER JOHN

6/3/2012

Rain poured over our heads as we walked to Cologne's central station. Our clothes and gear got drenched, and we sat in soggy shoes throughout the train ride to Berlin. I watched the German countryside through the window and it reminded me of the car rides from Madison to Saint Paul. The rolling Wisconsin hills are eerily similar to the German terrain. Perhaps that's why Germans settled in Wisconsin—it reminded them of home. However, home is the last thing on my mind.

Over the past few months, I fell in love with the album *Fear Fun* by Father John Misty, and it just so happens that he is playing a show in Berlin. Music is a powerful thing—it can resonate so deeply into one's very being that it puts one's very soul at ease. Father John Misty's music instigates such peace of mind within me, and I can't help but feel that this train ride to Berlin is a pilgrimage of sorts—this is my Mecca!

However, my group did not make reservations for our journey, and we were banished from our seats several times before settling into seats deep in steerage. Still, one's position on a train means nothing in sleep, which is precisely where I went. Rest deserves more attention from me, but how could I sleep on an adventure? As Ferris Bueller once said, "Life moves pretty fast. If you don't stop and look around once in a while, you could miss it." However, if one does not stop and rest once in a while, one might pass out. I fell asleep on the train and dreamt of my destination.

Jason and I were wetting our throats at the bar car when we noticed we were nearing Berlin. We quickly finished our Beck's and went to return to our seats. However, be it some strange custom or unbelievable impatience, almost every passenger was standing in the aisle with their suitcases in hand. What good does this accomplish? Everyone is getting to the station at the same time; you don't need to jump the gun! After about fifty "Excuse-mes,", we finally make it back to our seats, and just in time to get off in Berlin! We took the S-Bahn to our hostel and checked in with ease. We were informed that there was a pool and sauna, and the group decided to immediately make use of these accommodations. The pool water was too cold, so we headed to the sauna, which was filled with teenage New Zealanders with crazy stories and interesting laughs. Still, my mind could not be taken off the approaching event of that evening.

Jason, Terah, and I arrived at the Magnet Club on the edge of the Spree River just in time to catch the opening act's set. The musician was Ian Fisher, and his songs were sentimental and powerful—he's also a really nice guy (but we'll get to that later). We decided to buy his music and shake his hand, but as he handed Jason a CD, I heard the opening chords of Father John Misty's "Funtimes in Babylon." I ran into the room and found my idol perched up on the stage with guitar in hand. He didn't have a backing band—it was just him and his black Takamine guitar. The moment was surreal, and it changed me, but I am not sure how. Suddenly, I recognized that every bit of my life had led up to that moment—there in Berlin with Father John.

His songs weaved through the air in a lullaby of sorts, and I closed my eyes and opened my mind. But the music can't last forever, and it doesn't. My idol exited the stage and sat on a table, and I slowly made my way toward him. I extended my hand, and he extended his. I didn't know what to say. He smiled, and then it hit me— the music never stops, the adventure is never-ending, the pilgrimage is but a part of the journey, and mine is not over yet.

5: AM I STILL ILL?

6/6/2012

Today was the first of the dial classes, and Battleground started off with a bang! My class met in front of the Reichstag and discussed the events leading up to the Great War. Strange how one building can have so many histories. The Reichstag was both the headquarters of Wilhelm II, and one fiery reason for the Nazis' power grab in 1933.

How eerie it was to have the lecture's content reflect the very things I stared at! After our discussion, we headed over to the site of Hitler's bunker, which is now just a parking lot. What a nuisance it must be to be a regular at that lot—it must see more foot traffic than car traffic! After examining a layout of the bunker, we went down the street for lunch. The place we flocked to was a tourist trap, but they made damn good currywurst! Unfortunately, a virus did a number on my energy, and I spent the remainder of the day in quarantine in my room. However, I watched *A Bridge Too Far* about Operation Market Garden at the end of WWII and started *The Guns of August,* so my cold did not hinder learning!

6/7/2012

Waking up this morning was much easier than I anticipated. My fever had gone away completely, and I finally felt like myself again. The history group met at the German History Museum, and we went in after Cam's lecture on the Battle of the Somme and America's role in the Great War. The museum itself is massive—how else can one hope to illustrate a culture's entire history in one room? There were so many things to see and read that I

240

just about burned myself out by the 1848 exhibit!

After wandering through the entire thing, some highlights included: Napoleon's hat and sword found at Waterloo, Otto Bismarck's military garb, and the Auschwitz model of the gas chamber and crematorium. As it turns out, the German people have quite an interesting past!

Everyone in the group took the museum at a different pace, so I came out of it alone. It was then that I realized how confident I had become with the area. I had gone from oblivious gawking tourist to semi-confident gawking tourist! I expertly made my way back to Alexanderplatz for my grub of choice (Doner kebab), when I heard reggae music from the plaza. Kebab in hand, I followed the good vibes all the way to a string of tents lined up in the center of Alexanderplatz. It was not difficult to find the source of the reggae, and I soon found myself face to face with a grinning man in Rastafarian colors surrounded by old vinyl in plastic bins. I quickly snarfed down the remnants of the kebab and began to peruse through the cheerful titles of the old 33s. The man came up to me and started to speak German in a thick Jamaican accent, but I smiled meekly and said "English?"

His face lit up as he said "Jah mon!" It turns out that this cat's name was Joe Blue, and he had been traveling across Europe with several duffel bags of reggae records in order to spread the word of Rasta. I liked his style, so I picked up a record from The Lone Ranger called *The Other Side of Dub*. I suppose everyone is on a mission, but you'd be tough pressed to find someone with a groovier goal than Joe Blue.

6: TWO GATES

6/9/2012

Today was the day I went to the Sachsenhausen concentration camp. I had been nervous about this day all week, and honestly, I had no idea what I was in for. Andy set the tone for that day with a powerful lecture, and I nearly cried at the end when he quoted Anne Frank saying, "That I believe there is still goodness in the world."

Our tour guide met us in the lobby of our hostel, and we set off for the station. The train to Oranienburg was packed to the brim, but the group stayed in high spirits and Brittany led us through some games to pass the time. I was laughing up until I thought about what this trip meant for so many people all those years ago. Such a somber journey juxtaposed with Brittany's whimsical games made me feel melancholy to the point of making my stomach turn. My how the times have changed.

We left the train and walked through town. Our guide explained how the camp had been built in the center of town, and it amazed me how something so awful could be integrated so easily into daily life. Hell, there was a road connecting both sides of town that went right through the camp! Scarier still is the looming Tower A—its dark secret wrapped up in white, how innocent it looks. *Work will make you free,* suggests the gate, but only after you enter can you see how backwards this statement is—both figuratively and physically.

How can I describe the wind rushing through the field where the barracks once stood? Haunting, like a chorus of ghosts singing a sorrowful tune, and powerful, like an invisible palm pushing your body back with a rigid intensity. Stranger still that the remains of the crematorium stand in ashes, in the all-encompassing silence of Station Z. It makes me worry knowing what

242

humans are capable of doing. How can people be driven to such a place? Every man must ultimately face himself. After today, I am further convinced that the ruins of the past stand tall in relevance.

I returned to the hostel exhausted. Both mind and body were weak, but I knew that tonight, my last in Berlin, would bring about adventure. Germany and Portugal went head to head in the premier game of the Euro Cup for both teams. Dan, Jason, and I headed out for a beer and a kebab, all the while keeping our eyes out for cheap German garb. We found a tourist trap selling knock-off German jerseys for cheap on the sly, and picked up a few so as to mask our tourist tendencies. Unfortunately, we instantly came to realize that we now looked like über-tourists in our cheap, matching German jerseys. However, we embraced it, and headed down towards the Brandenburg Gate.

At this point, we had run into Kendall, Lynn, Brittany, and Ray, who happened to be wearing the same cheaply made and ill-fitting jerseys. Our happy band of Americans walked down to the entrance to the street behind the gate and became engulfed by the mass of Germany supporters who filled the streets with black, yellow, and red.

Never will I forget the chaos that erupted when Germany scored the only goal of the game! The noise of the screams was deafening. Dan gave the crowd a run for its money when he hopped on Jason's shoulders and began belting out "Deutschland" over and over. This lasted up until Dan's frantic fist bumps to the sky proved to be too much for Jason's balance, and the pair collapsed onto the street in a heap of cheap jerseys and enthusiasm. A beer at a nearby shop fixed the slight scrapes of both parties, and all was well.

Still, I can't help but think of where this day started and where it ended. Remarkable, how two gates can lead into such different worlds.

7: THE PEACOCKS OF PRAGUE

6/12/2012

My second independent travel has undoubtedly been a success. Everything from the people, food, and spectacular sights of Prague have pleased my traveler's needs. And what better way to begin our Czech-filled days than with a lighthearted train ride from Berlin?

Jason, Haddy, and I arrived in an empty cabin, but it was clear that the train was bound to fill up. Sure enough, two girls brandishing outlandishly large backpacks asked in high-pitched British accents if the seats around us were available. We confirmed the vacancy of the seats and dived into a conversation that lasted for the entirety of the trip. We talked about our respective trips and our backgrounds; we compared scars and played cards; we talked about the differing tax structures of our governments and offered up our favorite beers. Once we arrived in Prague, we exchanged information and agreed to meet up later for an urban adventure.

Lugging our gear through downtown was surreal—the many ancient buildings loomed over our spinning heads as if we were somehow thrust into a new-age fairytale. We popped into our hostel only long enough to drop off our things before we embarked back into the city. It was freeing to find yourself in a foreign place with no other agenda than your own, but the weight of travel bogged down my eyelids to the point of no return, and I decided to return to the hostel after a Doner kebab and a beer. However, sleep is no waste of time, and I give myself a pat on the back when I woke up the next morning fully recharged.

My companions were in a similar state, and after a hardy Czech breakfast we decided to venture across the river to Prague Castle. One item of note—there was a garden at the bottom of the hill leading up to the castle, and it doubled as a war memorial and an aviary. Several peacocks called this garden home, one of which was one of the most magnificent creatures I have ever seen. Its intricate white feathers stood around five feet tall when it chose to display them. At the time we saw it, an inconsiderate Russian man had provoked the creature to its magnificent state in an attempt to impress the girl accompanying him. The peacock was not enjoying the Russian's persistent taunting, and gave out an ear-curdling squeal in defense. After hearing the great squawk, no one attempted to prod the creature for its display.

The castle itself was not so much a castle as it was a complex. A self-guided tour of the impressive set of buildings was cheap with our student IDs, and we made use of our discount (to the detriment of our feet). We walked through the great Gothic church, wandered through the room where pro-Habsburg elites were thrown out of a window, starting the Thirty Years' War, and even meandered down Golden Lane, where we looked at medieval armor and Jason shot a crossbow.

By the time we made it back to our hostel, we were already late to meet up with the London girls from the train! So we devoured some Chinese food and went to the Prague astronomical clock, where we found our foreign friends waiting. A few drinks later, talk of a ghost walk appeared out of thin air, and soon we found ourselves being paraded downtown by a drunk man in a monk costume telling ghost stories while cracking sexist jokes. The tour ended abruptly when our guide took off his robes in a "That's all, folks!" sort of way and left for a pub. We did the same, but soon found ourselves back at their hostel bar playing cards into the wee hours of the night. If only every night could be so good!

However, a bulky man with deep-set eyes and a crooked frown raised his figurative feathers and squawked at us to vacate the bar. We agreed to his demands, for we had learned not to provoke the peacocks of Prague.

8: OH, THE PLACES YOU'LL SLEEP

6/13/2012

My traveling troupe took a train to Munich in hopes of spending one last German afternoon on our trip. The six hour endeavor passed by in a haze of sleep and reading, so the trip seemed much faster than it was. However, the cramped reality of a night train to Paris gnawed at my nerves as the Munich Main Train Station came into view. I reminded myself to live in the moment, regardless of the night's delight—and hell, it could be fun.

It was a weight off our shoulders to stow our bags in a locker in the station, and the freeing feeling fought off my anxiety—the coffee from Starbucks helped too.

Our gang of three left the station and headed across the street to the kebab shop. (After Berlin, I came to terms with my kebab addiction, and I had been fueling it ever since.) With a delicious Doner in my belly, I felt ready to take on the world, or at least Munich. Still, how can one see a city in an afternoon? It is surely an impossible task, so we did not set our goals so lofty. Instead, we decided to find an authentic German beer garden, which, as it turns out, wasn't hard at all. With a "mosse" in hand, I watched Denmark play Portugal on a big screen. Loads of folks decked out in white, red, and yellow filtered in as the contents of my glass mug shrank in size. The German squad was set to take on Holland that night, and although it was sure to be a good game, we had a train to catch.

{

Jason opened the door to our couchette/sleeping cabin on the train and his jaw dropped. He turned to Haddy and myself, and I knew it wasn't good. Our little slice of heaven housed six beds in what appeared to be a walk-in closet, and the space did not get any bigger once we brought our gear in. We shared the cabin with a Parisian couple who had been visiting friends in Munich. They were nice enough, but our relationship became strained when I opened the door to find the woman completely pantless in the middle of changing into her pj's—or at least that's what I think she was doing, I didn't stick around to find out. Besides, Jason and I weren't ready for bed, so we brought a few German beers out into the hallway and watched the dim landscape rip by our eyes in a flash of drunken light.

I awoke in the middle bunk in the light of the morning, very confused and a little hungover. Haddy informed me that the train was ten minutes outside of Paris, so I scrambled down to the floor to pack my things. Before I could say, "Where is my toothbrush?" the train had pulled into Gare de l'Est. With a little coffee and a pain au chocolat, my morale was restored in that stumbling Parisian morning.

Soon we were on a semi-crowded Metro on our way to Place d'italie, and the memory of traveling with my dad and brother came rushing back. How long had it been since I put my first Metro billet into a gate? How impossible those underground trains had seemed back then—before the fear of a cave-in was replaced with the fear of pickpockets.

The squeaking brakes of the Metro halted my nostalgia, and all of a sudden I was standing on the platform of Place d'italie, realizing that the coffee had worn off. I caught sight of a man dressed in fluorescent rags sleeping next to a vending machine. I envied his sleep, but not his hygiene. Well, at least he had more room than the night train's couchette.

9: EMBRACE YOUR INNER TOURIST

6/14/2012

This first real day in Paris flew by. Walking through the city streets was like calling an old friend after a few years of silence—we had both grown, but somehow there was still a sense of comfort. The sights were just about the same, but my perspective had undoubtedly changed. I took the metro to the Arc De Triomphe with Jason and Terah on our first night, and Napoleon's pride was still where it has always been, but something was different.

The arc was something I'd seen many times, but what had simply been an impressive building was now a symbol of an empire. The élan, or fighting spirit, that General Foch had impressed upon the French army in the Great War was woven into the arc itself. While standing in its shadow, I couldn't help but think what generals and soldiers had thought about as they stared up the arc. Tourist trap or not, the Arc De Triomphe inspired generations of Frenchman to defend their country.

Still, there are things that I had never seen in Paris. The Musée d'Orsay was one such place, but I finally got the chance to go that day. The museum was located in an old train station that had been converted to house many paintings and furniture now viewed by spectators from all over the world. I was one such visitor today with the needle group, and I was blown away.

While visiting the Van Gogh Museum in Amsterdam, I stumbled upon a sketch that I fell in love with. A girl lies on a bed, chest first, and stares at the viewer with the most somber and mystifying look. I simply have never seen a look like it. The artist's name is Henri de Toulouse-Lautrec, and there is an entire gallery at the Musée d'Orsay dedicated to his work.

Now, I should say that I have an interesting technique in terms of my viewing at art-oriented museums. When I find something that truly resonates within me, I will stare at it until I come to understand where the meaning comes from. This can take a long time, so I don't necessarily get through an entire museum . . . I probably spent an hour and a half in the Toulouse-Lautrec room. I felt power in almost every one of his pieces. I have never felt so connected to an artist.

I looked up some quotes of his, and I feel they are as relevant as anything: "I paint what is true and not what is ideal. The idealist thinks in the fantastical, the realist thinks in truth." He also has another quote concerning the nature of drink ("Of course one should not drink much, but often"), but I like it for reasons not concerning art whatsoever.

Jumping ahead to later that night, my troupe decided to embrace our tourist status, and so we walked to the Eiffel Tower. While walking through the compressed streets guarded by looming apartment buildings, I kept thinking that the tower would appear around every corner. Jason led the way, and all of a sudden he turned at us and smiled. A few steps further, and the fabled construct of warped steel appeared, illuminated with a soft yellow glow against the calm Parisian skyline.

Tourists will be tourists, so we snapped pictures and waited for the hourly display of sparkles. When the clock hit 11 (or shall I say 23?) the steel creature displayed its foreigner-pleasing flickering nature. I couldn't tell what flashed more, the tower, or the countless cameras lining its perimeter. We had our share of shots snapped, and headed over to the park. Here we bought wine from one of the many shady salesmen wandering around, carrying bottles in hand and cigarettes in pockets.

The salesmen aren't too friendly, though, and a group of two began harassing a circle of American students next to us. This confrontation stopped when a chubby baton-wielding police officer ran towards the wine-wielding salesmen, and everyone trying to sell a bottle made a mad dash towards the opposite end of the park. There must have been upwards of thirty sprinting salesman, but the police officer didn't catch a single one—he gave up when they scattered and he ran out of breath.

We started talking with the students over our illegally obtained beverages, and shared experiences and adventures. They were all fashion students doing a three-week course in Paris, and their posh attire and love for all things tobacco gave away their field of study before they said anything. Only a few of them figuratively stuck their noses in the air, so we got along pretty well. But once the wine was done and the tower made its final dazzling display for the day, we knew we should be getting home.

Upon our return to the hostel we ran into two folks around our age, so we began to chat. The boy's name was Sean—he was originally from Ireland, but he had been away for the past two years teaching English in South Korea. He decided to take three days in Paris before returning to Ireland. The girl's name was Ella—her father was a championship kickboxer, and their family moved around from Israel to Australia and back following his career. Although the Oops! Hostel has some sketchy rules about when we can be in our rooms, I had already met so many cool people there!

The places were great, but the people were better. I finally went to bed at God knows when, but there are some conversations that deserve to be seen through.

10: THE ROAD TO VERDUN

6/17/2012

Today the Battleground class went to Verdun, one of the bloodiest battlefields of the Great War. We woke up early and caught a morning train to Meuse, where we hopped on a bus to Verdun. I passed these trips catching up on sleep—one realizes the importance of naps when burning the candle at both ends. A Parisian night is not to be missed, but the same is true for class, and the resulting midday unconscious hours were welcomed by yours truly. However, I was very much awake as I stood outside the tiny Verdun train station.

Hannah needed a taxi to the tourist office where we would catch our tour bus, so I led the rest of the group across town on foot. My dad had taken my brother and me there when we were younger, so I had an idea of where to go. However, Hannah and Cam weren't at the office when we got there. It turns out that no cabs were running that day (it was Sunday), and we were running out of time till the tour. Anna Jo and I went outside in search of someone who might be able to give Hannah and Cam a lift from the station. I was just about to give up when Anna Jo flagged down a pair of men in the parking lot. I ran over and dug deep into my bag of French vocab in order to explain the situation. One of the men agreed to help, and I soon found myself riding shotgun in his car as we blasted reggae towards the train station. Add another point for humanity!

After picking up a strange bottle of what appeared to be fizzy nectarine-lemonade, we boarded the bus and took off down the road to the battlefield. How eerie to think of the constant flow of soldiers and supplies coming in and out of the battle on that very road . . .

Our first stop was a museum on the edge of the destroyed town of Fuery, where we saw a recreation of a trench along with many relics. The museum was fine and dandy, but it was the town of Fuery itself that stood out. Cam led the class along a path through the field of craters and shattered bricks. Some craters held completely still pools of water, which reflected the green trees hovering above. It was an eerie sight—the remnants of man versus nature. Although the area was beautiful, there were reminders of the battle all around. Some of these reminders were relics, and Ray began a hunt for such objects when he happened upon a hundred-year-old French-made bullet on the side of the road.

I decided to stray from the beaten path to explore the lesser-traveled craters. In one such hole, I happened upon a grenade. I stared at it for a while in disbelief. How ironic, that the tiny beast should rest in the serenity of the forest that grew around the destruction caused by its brethren! In a moment of overpowering curiosity, I reached out and picked it up. I can't explain why I did it—even now it doesn't make sense to me. Still, in that moment, I had to hold it in my hand. Time had worn down the ridges and forced a crack down its side, but it still felt heavy in my hand. Who had been the last to hold it? Who had thrown it? It didn't detonate; it had failed— would someone have died? Who was trying to kill who? But a better question is why. I brought the grenade down the trail and brought the class over to see it. Cam, who was rightly dumbfounded as to why I had disturbed the thing, took a picture of it lying in the grass and we left.

I could go on about Verdun for ages, but the symbolism of the grenade sums up my thoughts fairly well. The Great War was destruction, mass murder for power, and the loss of an entire generation. The grenade was the assassination Franz Ferdinand, who met his fate when, by chance, his chauffer took a wrong turn down a dead-end street. What if the grenade hadn't exploded? Even now, a beautiful forest grows over Fuery.

11: PARISIAN REGGAE AND SEE-THROUGH ME

6/19/2012

I ushered in Tuesday earlier than most, with another raucous night at the Eiffel Tower. Over my stay at the Oops! Hostel, I've become good friends with Sean, but our schedules did not align for a night on the town until Monday. So Dan and I took the Metro to Bir-Hakeim in hopes of meeting up with him at the tower.

It didn't take long to spot the group in the park, so we opened our wine and began to discuss the contents of our minds. However, I couldn't dedicate my full attention to the conversation—the group next to us had a full-on jam going, consisting of a guitar and several makeshift percussion pieces. I envied their full chords and smiling vocals, which often broke into laughing fits. Besides, I was suffering from guitar withdrawal, and I would do anything to play! I brought up the idea of converging our groups, but the response was hesitant, so I walked over and joined in the jam, scratching a water bottle to the beat. The song ended with smiles, and I was handed one of the real percussion instruments.

I slowly made my way up the ranks until I was

handed the guitar. I warmed up my fingers, and soon the tune was raging. I broke into a reggae riff, and the percussion section joined in. The group consisted of two guys from Les Seychelles off of Madagascar and groups from Austria and Italy. Music is the great unifier!

Unfortunately, the night lasted well into the morning, so lecture was fine, but a little rough. We met up at the Roman Theatre and talked about Hitler's rise and fall from power. Cam's lecturing ability is at a point where I can be running on very little sleep and still be completely enthralled! A crepe-and-panini combo afterward boosted both my energy and my spirits as we geared up for the group discussion with Maurice Kling—an Auschwitz survivor.

We met up at the Jussieu Metro stop and patiently waited for Mr. Kling to arrive. Two men with cameras preceded him, ready and able to record the discussion. Soon enough, he appeared. Maurice is a vibrant man—he radiates energy, and he was all smiles as he led the group to the Roman Theatre. He explained the history of our discussion's venue as we walked through the Roman stones. We stopped by a set of stairs, and everyone sat down in front of Mr. Kling.

He then told his story, starting with his upbringing—how his father had owned a shop blocks away from the theatre, and how happy he had been at his school. His teachers loved him, but that didn't stop the Gestapo from arresting him one day in class. Maurice and his family were sent to Auschwitz, where his family was killed in Nazi gas chambers. However, he emphasized that his message is more important than his story. "Don't remember me," he said. "Remember them."

His words hit me like a freight train. He had dedicated his life to telling his story, but really, it's not his story. "See through me," he said. "The individual is nothing and the history, the story, is everything."

Maurice is a product of a hellish environment, one that we can't begin to imagine. However, there is so much for us to learn; the past lives within the future.

I left the discussion feeling dazed. Words are more potent than anything. I thought back to Bob's lecture in Amsterdam about the difference between strong and soft power—the idea may not be as evident as the tanks barreling down the street, but the idea will outlast the tank. As I walked back to the hostel, I thought about the soft power that I have instilled within my core, and the opinions and perspective I have formed in my life. So then how does something come to have meaning to me?

Throughout this trip I have been coming back to the connection between place and self. What gives place meaning—people. The ideas of society have shaped the earth into monuments of stone and steel, but without context, without culture, these objects would be meaningless. This is why history is relevant—to better understand the meaning of one's self, the human condition, we must study the efforts, the faults, and the truths of the past.

See through me.

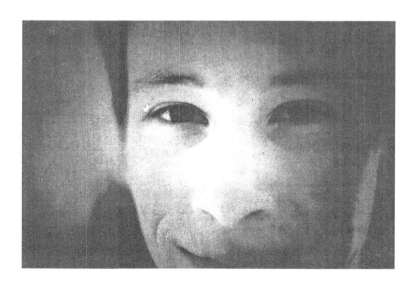

A FACEBOOK STATUS FROM OLA

You don't really ever need an excuse to visit this beauty. From where I live, you just need a free hour or so. But yesterday in particular, though, I really wanted to make sure I got over there.

I'm a sucker for dates. Not dates like, flowers, dinner, and a movie dates (though I do enjoy those as well) but I mean dates as in on the calendar. I don't know why, I just tend to remember them well, even though their commemoration often doesn't mean much other than another lap or half-lap around the sun. But for some reason I just feel a connection through them, and when a particularly important date comes up, I tend to spend the day reminiscing on the past, musing on what was, that day, a few laps around the sun ago.

So that was yesterday. Or rather, yesterday, two years ago. April 7, 2013. It was the last day that we had with him before everything happened, before the second hospital visit that he didn't get to walk out of. April 7th, two years ago, was an incredible day. It was sunny and beautiful and it was a Sunday that I spent with my sister and my boyfriend, and all the regulars of the place that was 220 College Court, procrastinating homework, hanging out, enjoying spring's sunshine.

After that, it rained for a week.

My sister got to meet him that day, for the first and last time. It was a day trip to Madison that came and went on a whim, and I'll never forget how I said "Hey, Henri! There's someone I want you to meet!" (we were half-speaking French to each other at that point, in celebration of my going to Paris as a graduation trip, only a month and a half away) and he poked his head out of the kitchen area, then came out and gave my sister an excited hug. And so they met, and she loved him, because how could she not? Everyone did! Everyone still does.

So that was April 7th. It was beautiful. It was Madison at its prime. Our group of friends at its prime. The next day was sunny too. I distinctly remember a phone conversation with my sister that morning, as I was bustling to class, and she told me how happy she was for me to finally have found my place in such an incredible group of people. To cherish them, and hold on to them, because I've got a hell of a support group. We didn't know it then, and we wouldn't learn for a few more hours, but he was already in a coma when that conversation happened. We had to rely on that support group earlier than expected.

It's that group that I've been missing a lot the last couple days. Like I said, I'm a sucker for dates, so the last week I've been mostly stuck in the past, musing on the last memories we made with him before they took place in a hospital room. Fake breaking up with Andrew on April Fool's Day, walking into 220 to see Nick and Henry who said "So you finally dumped his ass!", legs flailing with laughter. Seeing him at the bus stop, shouting his name, and both of us dancing around for no reason. I remember thinking I would regret it if I didn't shout his name and do something crazy, but I did it. And today, two years ago, is where we met that hospital room, and spent a few days there, before everything finally crashed like we so hoped it wouldn't. But I still try to think about the 7th as the last beautiful good one we had. Because as far as good days go, this was a really, really, good one.

So anyway, that's why I wanted to make April 7, 2015, a good day. And I did! I got errands done, went for a run in my favorite place, babysat for a few hours, then spent a good few hours underneath this tower, thinking about the past and the future and what's to come and what was. And how our new memories with him came to a sudden halt two years ago now, and what I might have said if you told me I'd be drinking red wine (yes, I have graduated from white to red, it was inevitable but only took a few months) on the Champ de Mars, among all the tourists and excited study abroad students, the men trying to sell mini Eiffel Towers and bottles of champagne. Don't worry, we brought our own wine—and I've got the real thing right in front of me. Anyway, two years ago, I'm not sure what I would have said had you told me I'd be living within half an hour of this tower today. Had you told him, he probably would have high-fived me and grinned, like he did when I told him my parents were taking me to Paris for graduation.

I'm sure I'll have more April 7ths in my life. I mean, symbolically, not literally (though I do hope I will have more literal April 7ths as well). For me it's come to symbolize the end of something so great, but you don't know it's the end until it's already far away from you. A world away. An entire life away, even. It's not the same as moving away to another place, and feeling nostalgic for the place you're moving from, because you know that's the end of your chapter there. No, April 7th is a day that is the last page of an incredible, welcoming, sincere chapter in my life, and I never knew that until it was already too late. Until it was April 10th, really. I'll always hold onto the 7th though. It's too good a chapter to focus on the first page of the next one.

Just like that day two years ago, yesterday was a good day, a beautiful day, a day I'll remember, probably to a weird degree of specificity. And I'm happy for that. Just remember—you never need an excuse to drink or even just sit under the Tour Eiffel. But if you're commemorating a friend who you loved and continue to miss, and who loved the city and the language and his friends—it's a damn good excuse.

Ola Lisowski
April 8, 2015

Salut, Henri,

I'm flying to Paris tonight! Gunnar gave me the best idea—I'm bringing a lock and finding that bridge that everyone puts locks on, I'm writing your name all over, locking it on there, and throwing the key in the Seine.

Then part of you can be in Paris forever. In the city of lights forever. What a beautiful thought.

Loving and missing you always, Henri. Tu me manques toujours.

Ola Lisowski
May 20, 2013

(Zack) If you've just tuned in for some odd reason, we've been here for three hours, since midnight.

(Henry): Three glorious hours.

(Max): Three sweaty hours.

(Henry): What happens in the studio, stays in the studio, you don't talk about it on the air—that's like Rule #1. Remember that contract I made you sign?

(Max): Rule #2: there are no rules.

(Zack): Rule #3: rock and roll.

(Henry): Rock and roll. That should be Rule #1.

(Max): Rule #4: keep on rocking in the free world.

(Zack): This is too many rules.

(Henry): Yeah I don't like it. Because rock and roll is all about breaking the rules, and that's what we're all about here at Strange Groove. We're about breaking rules and clapping hands into microphones.

(Zack): Did you hear that? That was the sound of rules being broken.

(Henry): That's right. Just a big old rule snapped right in half.

Henry, Max Fisher, and
Zack Stafford on Strange Groove.
The end of a three-hour show.

The Blue Towel Troupe Origin Story

One night I was playing bass in my room with my door open. Henry had just gotten out of the shower when he walked by, wearing only a towel. He saw me playing and said, "You stay right there!" Then he ran next door to his room and grabbed his guitar. He came back and said, "There's no time to put clothes on, we're jamming right here, right now." So he sat in a chair in his blue towel, and we jammed, making up everything as we went along.

I was pretty familiar with improvisation, but my primary instrument was the trumpet, and I had only ever played bass with strict, predetermined written lines. Playing with Henry that night was the first time that I was able to play more freely and make it up as I went along. Henry would name a key, and we'd jam as if we'd played it a thousand times before. Eventually, Henry started adding lyrics that he made up on the spot, a skill that had always amazed me. We played for the better part of forty-five minutes, and ended up accumulating a substantial audience.

Combined with his virtuoso guitar skills, I could tell that I was in the presence of someone incredible. We heard a knock on the door, and it was a house-fellow telling us that quiet hours started twenty minutes ago, and we had to keep the noise down.

That's what he had intended to say, anyway. He was thrown off mid-sentence by the sight of Henry playing guitar wearing only a towel. He stuttered in confusion for about ten seconds, then regained his composure, and politely asked us to quiet down, in between bouts of giggling.

That was not the last time we would share a jam under those circumstances—it was repeated the following night. But that time, our floormate Alex Schacherl joined us with his guitar. Another person on our floor, Monica Nigon, was part of the audience that night—until she went back to her room and grabbed her violin. The four of us played some Irish folk songs and Mumford and Sons tunes, until we were again waylaid by the house-fellows for quiet hours. But it was that night that we resolved to make ourselves a group. I called my high school friend, Matt Kline, who lived on the floor below us, to play piano, and the Blue Towel Troupe was born.

—Andy Kerber

Alex Schacherl, guitar
Henry Mackaman, guitar
Andy Kerber, bass
Matthew Kline, piano
Monica Nigon, violin

Handmade Phantom Vibration albums

kids
Growing
Aged

STILLNESS

Phantom Vibration

Soon enough we'll be crestfallen
A nest fallen
A tired troupe
But till that day, a motely bunch,
We'll soldier on, no heads will droop.

The stillness in the soil
Spread your fingers
Sink in your claws.

We'll rest till dusk
When we'll arise
To chase the dawn.

The summer sun is now rising
With the fervor to part the clouds,
As it pushes through the shell of the smog,
Warmth ebbs through this tepid dream,
A geyser's vigor with jetting steam.

Long since we've laid our packs down
While memories abide.

In foreign tides
We'll launch ourselves
Towards clear skies.

Phantom Vibration t-shirt designed by
Dan Clinton-McCausland.

SO I PLAYED
GUITAR ALL
NIGHT LONG
UNTIL I BROKE
A HEART
STRING
TIME WILL
HEAL ALL MY
WOUNDS
BUT IT DOESN'T
HURT TO SING
NO, IT DOESN'T
HURT TO SING.

-LYRICS BY HENRY

"Phantom Vacation"
November 2012

aged

chimes | sapience

silver tongue | river rock

recorded, mixed, mastered
by henry mackaman at
acid sweat lodge
saint paul, mn

thanks

mickey davis , lily parmenter , samilee moody,
marlys mandaville, taman at chamber of secrets, schuyler
and everyone at the 108, eli flasher at 7th street, allie
dougharty & micael berhane at WFCI, clara salyer,
cody nelson, amanda reeder, caleigh souhan, chase mathey,
brody howard & all at Radio K, caitlin kidder, genevieve oliver,
CP220 , claudia chenard, the white house evon interns,
lus/jon/ john/matt & matt, our families, dent may, &
Noel Fielding

ALBUM COVERS

PHANTOM | VIBRATION

I'm not one of those composers/lyricists who can write a song in one day. If I'm really on a roll, I might draft 90 percent of it, but it may take a steamy shower two days later to make me realize that the chorus needs one more phrase. It may take a frustrating car trip to make me realize that a song has more expressive potential than I thought. And every once in a while, it takes significantly more than that. Until I wrote 'Grace,' I didn't know how much more.

Admittedly, I'd assigned myself a challenging task. Many of my previous songs touched on ideas like forgiveness, compassion, and grace, but writing an entire song about such a concept was a whole different matter. In addition, the grace I wanted to sing about is not what people usually consider grace to be, namely a gift bestowed upon humans by God. To me, grace is much broader than that. It is something we offer to each other and ourselves and the whole unpredictable and often disappointing world, over and over again, so that we can stay awake and alive and—somehow, against all odds—in a state of love. How to say all that in a song?

After five years of sporadic writing and rewriting and re-rewriting, I had pretty much given up on the project. Then three years ago—suddenly, devastatingly— on the most beautiful April day, my son Simon's friend Henry became infected by a strain of meningitis for which no vaccine existed, and nobody realized it until it was too late to save his life. The shock was abrupt and fathomless and impossible. I wandered around the house and made cup after cup of tea I didn't drink, remembering those two boys jamming their hearts out in the rock bands they had formed together in middle and high school. And then after a while I sat down at the piano. I knew exactly what I wanted to say about grace. I don't imagine that I'll ever hear 'Grace' without being reminded of the unbearable fragility of life, but I no longer feel angry that something beautiful was conceived because of Henry's death. The only alternative to that would be for nothing beautiful to have happened. To be left with only pain and fear and grief.

This way, instead: music, compassion, love, grace.

Elizabeth Alexander

GRACE

Elizabeth Alexander

It's how I hold my head up after I have
missed the mark,
It's how I know I'm loved when things are dark,
It's how I stand when I am feeling small,
How I stand again after a fall—
It's how I'm even standing here at all:
Some people call it Grace.

Falling down like rain on everyone,
So warm, like greetings from the sun,
Like a gentle snow it's making every surface glow.
And I know I didn't earn it:
That's how I know it's Grace.

It's how two people stay together through
the many years,
It's how a broken people sing again,
It's how a man can overcome his shame,
How a woman moves beyond her fears—
It's how I know that holy is my name.
We're all the same to Grace.

Falling down like rain on everyone,
So warm, like greetings from the sun,
Like a gentle snow it's making every surface glow.
And I didn't have to earn it.
No, I didn't have to earn it:

I didn't have to earn it through a word or
through a deed,
Or through a trial or through a creed,
Or by denying what I need.
I only had to reach out my hand, and it was there.
But still it cannot take away the truths I have to face.
Oh no, that's not how it works with Grace.

Falling down like rain on everyone,
So warm, like greetings from the sun,
Like a gentle snow it's making every surface glow.
And I know I didn't earn it.
No, I didn't have to earn it.
I didn't have to earn it:
That's how I know it's Grace.

A BIRTHDAY STATUS FOR HENRY, FROM TRENT

Happy birthday, Henry. With everything that's been happening these past few days, I must admit that being reminded of just how much I miss you was a bit overwhelming. But rather than wallow with sadness, I want to celebrate the wisdom you passed on to me and so many others.

I was reflecting today and came to realize that losing you was a very defining moment in my life, both intellectually and artistically. Before you passed, I knew that I wanted to study genetics but was more interested in the biology of evolution and development. After losing you, I remember feeling despair. I didn't understand why you were taken—it was so unfair, it was so random.

Seeing the waves of remorse pass through the community of family and friends around you, then into the larger community at whole was devastating . . . and I think that this event subconsciously pushed me into studying infectious diseases. Soon after you passed, I joined a research lab on campus studying bacterial pathogenesis. This lead me to take a job in academic research of host/

pathogen genetics after graduating with the intention of returning to graduate school to obtain a PhD.

So, though I would trade the world to hang out one more time . . . because I can't, all I can do is thank you, Henry. Thank you for giving purpose to what started as a curiosity. I hope I can somehow honor your life by bringing your memory with me as I keep researching.

You were the single most influential musician in my life. I remember living with you in College Park, watching you record and mix Phantom Vibration mix tapes from start to finish. Before we met, I knew the basics of recording, but seeing how much passion you sunk into your work truly inspired me. You listened so closely . . . your ears so trained despite being nineteen. Every detail of the music and mix was intentional, all of the dynamic terrain was strategically planned. I had never seen anything like it. I distinctly remember thinking, wow . . . I have to catch up to Henry!

I began obsessing over music production. I started collecting gear and lugging it with me between each apartment I moved to over the years. Eventually I built out a fully functional home studio where I now record myself and other bands. None of this would have been possible without you giving me that pirated ProTools copy years ago, so thank you, friend. Again, I would give anything to hear your music at twenty-five, but all I can do is hope to honor your life as I keep writing and releasing music.

Tonight, rather than stressing about the state of our country, I get to celebrate your life with all of the other friends whom you inspired just like me. You created a family, Henry. We all owe you so much. Here's to you, friend. Gone but never forgotten, you live on through us.

Trent Prall

EVERY MAN NEEDS A COMPANION

Dean Allbrook drove himself to the hospital

in a coughing fit, holding the wheel in one hand and a handkerchief in the other. Although his vision had been dulled by eighty years of use, he could see spots of red scattered on the white linen. The Mercedes careened in the right lane like a pinball, narrowly avoiding a speeding taxi driven by a husky man who managed to honk his horn and erect his middle finger in one fluid motion. Dean failed to hear the horn over the chattering of his teeth and continued barreling down 12th Street, ten clicks over the speed limit. He dropped the handkerchief and gripped his chest, searching for the knot of pain welled up inside his lungs.

Although he had been living with the persistent wheezes and shivers for over a week, he had convinced himself that seeing a doctor was an expensive admission of defeat. But he had waited too long. That morning had brought about an incalculable hurt, which had forced him into his car even before the newspaper arrived. The dull pain of yesterday had become a lion's roar, and each hacking cough felt like a famished fang digging into his ribs.

The Mercedes turned right off of 12th Street into a paved graveyard of abandoned department stores and derelict pizza chains, which stood as solemn spectators lining the perimeter of the cracked concrete. The parking lots of downtown Quincy, Illinois had been graciously doled out by optimistic city planners fifteen years earlier, when the thought of the Ford plant shutting down was as laughable as the Cubs winning the pennant. Now the lots were used for shortcuts and drug deals, where the rules of the road had long ago been replaced by anarchy. Dean feared the doped-up delinquents who spent their days doing donuts outside the deserted superstores, and he was relieved to find that he was alone as he sped in a straight shot towards the hospital.

The route was not without peril, though. Pitfalls came in the form of potholes, one of which swallowed the Mercedes' front right wheel. Dean cursed as the car bounced violently and downshifted into second gear. The engine sputtered as he coughed into his hand and straightened out his tires. "I'm sorry about that," he said. "I'm not the driver I used to be."

He patted the dashboard in front of the empty passenger seat and smiled to himself, unaware that the gesture would leave dabs of red on the tan leather. Dean licked the blood off his hand and tried to wipe away the stain with his palm, but only managed to spread the red around. Fuck, he thought as he brought the Mercedes to a screeching halt. He hastily pulled off his sweater vest and began scrubbing the red patch with gray cotton, coughing violently as he worked.

A stain was unacceptable. Dean had always been sure to keep his car clean, and even though thirty years had passed, it looked just like it did when he drove it off the lot in 1979. He had fought for it; Laura had been skeptical, but he assured her they could pay for both the car and the baby once his big commission came through. Most of the money was gone in a matter of hours, but he had never been happier as he drove his ripened wife to the hospital. Finally, he had what he wanted, and he would never let it go.

Dean soon found himself engulfed in the shadow of Blessing Hospital, which stood as an island over the sea of parking lots. The thumping pain in his chest forced his foot further onto the accelerator as he navigated the paved loop in front of the ER. He stopped in front of the glass double doors and killed the engine with a trembling hand, hacking more phlegm from his tired lungs. Dean spat the bloody mixture onto the concrete as he opened the door, careful to avoid the car.

He approached a young man leaning on a garbage can, who smoked a cigarette like it was his life's calling. Dean looked him over up close, and although he wasn't sure why, the man reminded him of himself. A large B was embroidered on his blue collared shirt in thick red fabric, and the nametag hanging from his pocket read "Huck Cherin."

"You must be the valet," said Dean, fishing out

two twenties from his wallet. Huck nodded, the cigarette dangling dangerously from his mouth. "You treat this car like it was your life," Dean said as he put the money in the man's hand.

Huck took a deep drag from his cigarette, and exhaled slowly. "Understood," he said, shoving the money in his pocket. Dean looked him in the eye and nodded before another round of piercing coughs materialized. Huck took the keys, and Dean watched as the temporary valet slid into his baby, firmly gripping the wheel while teasing the ignition to life. The Mercedes purred forward, easily gliding over the pavement. Dean stood outside the double doors long enough to watch it plunge into the mouth of the unnecessary parking ramp, and a pain independent of his lungs stung him as he lost sight of the car and opened the door.

Upon arriving at the front desk, Dean was greeted by a nurse who gave him a smile and a clipboard. Her light blond hair was tucked in a bun behind her narrow head, and her baggy blue eyes held a sad gaze at his frail frame.

I could have had her if I were younger, Dean thought, eyeing her. He would grin and ask her if she could schedule an operation to repair his broken heart. She would act annoyed, and laugh to herself, but Dean would take a pen from her desk and scribble down his number. He would race off in his Mercedes, knowing that she would call. But that was before time had stretched his skin and stained his smile, and now he could only have her in his head.

The ambient sniffles and guttural hacks filled the silence between them, and the nurse held her smile even though she saw that a line had formed behind the sad old man. Dean remained rooted. He hadn't noticed it before, but it was clear to him now that this nurse had Laura's teeth. He squinted at them, noticing the pronounced canines, the slight overbite, and the yellow tinge from too many caffeinated mornings—they were almost identical.

Dean felt a hurt in his heart as he looked down at the clipboard and then back up at the nurse. The familiar tickle returned to his chest, and he hacked up more bloody phlegm, which hurtled uncontrollably from his mouth onto the clipboard. He regained his composure and handed the spotted red sheet to the nurse, who was no longer smiling.

After Dean's third day at the hospital, Dr. Collider told him that the mucus build-up in his lungs was threatening his life. "Pneumonia is not a laughing matter," the doctor had said, but Dean chuckled and told him he had nothing to worry about.

This doctor doesn't know anything, Dean thought. Pneumonia is no cause for concern. He remembered that Jane had it when she was four or five, how Laura had been too worried to sleep, and how she had been awake when he came home at three in morning, crying in their bed. Everything had been fine, though.

"You're going to die," said Dr. Collider.

"So are you," said Dean.

The doctor gritted his teeth, gave him a grim nod, and swiped the bran muffin on the end table as he turned to leave. Dean was alone, but he was used to it. He had a supply of gin and cigars at his condo for company, but the hospital room held none of his possessions, save for the bloodied sweater vest, pale collared shirt, and wrinkled slacks hastily folded on a chair opposite the bed. He was forced to stare at the sad pile, all too aware that the clothes on the chair would be its only occupants.

When a nurse had asked for his emergency contacts, Dean didn't know what to say. The Allbrook family had stopped inviting him to events after the divorce; Laura, he knew, had told them everything. His connections were the price of pleasure's company, and never before had he felt so stranded in solitude. Occasionally, tired nurses wandered in holding clipboards, hovering around the machinery in his peripheral vision. Dean noticed that the nurse working nights had Laura's hair, the same murky brown locks entombing her neck. Before long, he had conditioned himself to require a bedpan when her shift began. The nurse never said anything to him; she knew how lonely the terminals could be, and decided that her silence was the price of a fresh bedpan.

Dean cared more about the price of the liquid antibiotics Dr. Collider had prescribed, which weren't working. His breathing had gotten worse, and the scratchy sound of his consistent wheezes kept him up at night. Only cold water could console him. It seemed to dull the needles in his throat, and for a few seconds after each sip, he could convince himself that he was fine. But the nurses soon grew tired of refilling his glass only to empty his catheter, and they agreed amongst themselves to put a limit on his water intake. Dean soon caught on, and although the guttural racket he made in protest annoyed the hell out of them, they knew he couldn't keep it up for long, and they were right.

The water glass had been dry for hours as Dean lay awake on the fifth night. The sound of his labored breaths haunted the room with their resonance, and the four beige walls seemed to waver in the dark. He closed his eyes and tried to remember how to fall asleep, but his mind ran in circles around his head. He remembered how Laura had counted sheep every night, how she would whisper numbers in the dark until her lips became lifeless. He could feel her breathing through the box springs, but her body had never been warm to his touch. With only their bed in common, they were closest in sleep; his head filled with doubt, her head filled with sheep. How silly her sleeping technique had seemed back then, but now Dean was desperate to sleep like a dead man.

To his dismay, the sheep that he conjured had bored him awake. Instead he imagined a mistress's face, her hair, and her smile with skin smooth as a snake. But as soon as she appeared, she had been replaced by a different woman with a different face. Their count grew larger, and their features blurred together, as Dean's whispered numbers died in the dark.

"Dean?"

He opened his eyes.

"Dean Allbrook?" the familiar voice echoed through the veil of smoke encasing the hospital bed.

"Fire!" Dean yelled, frantically sitting up.

He looked down, and saw black water softly lapping at the sides of the mattress.

"Flood!" he shouted.

"Easy!" yelled the voice. "Stay still."

Dean looked from side to side, but he couldn't see through the smoke. The taste of stale tobacco filled his mouth as he inhaled in short rapid breaths, but it was like no cigar Dean had ever had.

"I want your story, but I'll make it easier for you. Just give me the beginning—your first memory." Huck looked him in the eye, his face like granite.

The sound of the paddle's strokes filled the silence between them. Dean put his hands together and twiddled his thumbs. He realized that it had been a long time since anyone had asked him questions.

"My folks had this TV set, really just a little piece of crap, but it was always on. They would sit in the living room after my pop got home from the bank and watch it for hours in the dark." Dean looked down at his busy thumbs. "I don't know how old I was, maybe four or five, but I remember walking into that living room, and watching my folks watch TV. My mom was smoking, and she had this little pink ashtray on her lap. My pop was drinking some whiskey or something, no ice. They didn't notice me."

Huck propelled the gondola forward with a forceful stroke.

"A happy family," he said, flicking his cigarette into the water.

"I didn't want to end up like them," said Dean.

Again Huck aggressively ran the paddle through the water, and again Dean fell forward.

"All family men are trapped," said Dean. "You only get one shot at life, so you need to look out for yourself."

Huck freed another cigarette from his pocket, and returned his gaze.

"You're right, that sounds like a lonely way to live," he said, bringing the paddle into the boat. Dean looked down at his wrinkled hands as the gondola ran aground.

"Here we are," said Huck, nodding towards the bow.

The front of the gondola had breached the wall of smoke hanging over the water, and through the clearing Dean saw his Mercedes parked past a gray beach. He looked back at Huck, who motioned for him to get out. Dean lifted his legs over the edge of the boat, and sunk his feet into the sand. He walked cautiously towards the car, but instead of inspecting its pale paint for scratches, he looked at the deserted parking lot before him.

He saw the cracked concrete fade into the foggy horizon, where two bounds of infinity had seemingly collided. He reached the car, and opened the door, but the old Mercedes felt emptier than before. The accelerator sat limp and lifeless at his feet as Dean stared down at the vacant passenger seat. He grabbed the wheel and turned the key, and the car came to life immediately. But Dean sat and stared straight ahead, unmoving. He turned towards the boat still parked on the shore, and saw Huck standing on the bow, watching him.

"Which way do I go?" Dean yelled over the engine.

Even at the distance, he could see Huck smile.

"You know, it doesn't really matter," he said, pushing the gondola back into the smoke.

||

TIME

Tired structures haunt the heart of the city.
Concrete hands crumble
to the soft brown earth.
Antique to young eyes,
ageless inquiries sting the sullen ear.
Great grief hangs off his wrinkled face,
torture in his eyes,
thick blood in his veins.
The gallant giver makes leave for the stars,
for no space
is worthy of time.

CRATER-GRAVE

I wanted nothing more
than to project the sands in my head
What else is there to do?
When all lives come to an end?
I wanted nothing more
than to work my way into her heart
What else is there to do
when nihilism becomes solitude?
But still I feel so melancholy
I must've grown up too soon
There is no more room in the cemetery
Still I dig a crater on the moon

Art by
Margaret Palmquist,
Henry's girlfriend.

LUCIDITY, COME BACK TO ME

OR "THAT'LL BE THE DAY"

I became my grandfather's caretaker

the summer after I graduated from college. My mother said I didn't have a choice, and she was right. We couldn't afford a nursing home, and both my older sisters had jobs and kids. My grandmother, who had occupied the position previously, was buried in a small cemetery outside of Des Moines in the spring of that year. At the funeral, my relatives mingled like teenagers forced to participate in an improv class. If it weren't for the family nose, none of us would have anything in common. Nevertheless, we exchanged false enthusiasm and forced smiles, but some tried harder than others: Aunt Mary made a speech and moved herself to tears (no one else cried), my mother stayed near the bar and became acquainted with Jack Daniels, and cousin Joseph crammed brownies down his slacks until his pants sagged. It's strange that I don't remember my grandfather there, but then again, neither does he.

"Simon! When is Carol coming back with those groceries?" he would say. At first I told him the truth—it was the right thing to do, he should know. I watched him relive Carol's death over and over, and things like that stay with you. After a while I decided to play his game; it was easier that way. "She'll be back soon."

He lived in an apartment on the outskirts of Des Moines, and I came to know the place well. The building was a three-story square block of bricks inhabited by a rotating array of four or five old folks. They called it home, but it was really a waiting room. The one-month lease wasn't fooling anyone. Mr. McGregor, a stubborn Army general from Alabama, lived on the left half of the first floor. He would sit on a green folding chair out on the lawn for hours, sipping away at a bottomless glass of gin and lemonade. He called his drink Tom Collins, but Ms. Macy called it devil juice. She lived on the first floor (the right side), and also spent her summer out on the lawn, substituting solitaire for gin. The two became fixtures of the front stoop, bickering and whining like foul-mouthed hyenas. There were several other tenants, but I hardly ever saw them. They haunted the third floor behind closed doors, their rooms silent as tombs. Sometimes I imagined their whispers seeping through the ceiling, but I tried not to think about them.

My grandfather and I didn't say much at first, but we got along all right. We lived in separate worlds, brought together by necessity. The time we spent in each other's company was like the awkward intersection of a Venn diagram—the contents of our respective circles remained secret for the most part. Maybe it was because we didn't spend time together when I was younger. No baseball games, no walks in the park, only a few scattered games of Scrabble. Back then, my vocabulary consisted of a few three-letter words (and several of the four-letter variety), but Grandpa didn't see this as a reason to take it easy on me. One of my first memories with him is an argument over Scrabble:

"Look here—Bezil, noun. It's a slanted surface."

"I don't believe you."

"It's right here in the dictionary! Can't you read?"

"Not really."

"Well then how have you been making words?"

"I've made 'cat' three times."

"Oh. Hey, don't forget to mark 26 points for Grandpa!"

However, as time passed and my vocabulary expanded, he became frustrated with the competition. When things took an unfavorable turn, he would grumble and pretend to have things to do, so we hardly ever saw a game all the way through.

"Look here—Hijra, noun. It refers to hermaphrodites in South Asia."

"I don't believe you."

"It's right here in the dictionary! Can't you read?"

"Not really, I don't have my glasses."

"Well then how have you been making words?"

"I have to drain the radiator."

Although he could be difficult, my tasks that summer were simple enough: drive him to the grocery store and the pharmacy in the morning, order coffee and a newspaper at Howard's diner on 4th Street, drive to the apartment for a nap, start a game of Scrabble (never finish), cook dinner, and repeat. "Just keep him alert," my mother would say. "Make him do a crossword every now and then." However, the hours my grandfather spent alert were few and far between. I had plenty of time on my hands, most of which I spent on an ugly floral couch in the living room reading stiff Hemingway paperbacks and frequently masturbating to the covers of dusty Buddy Holly records. How could I resist those sleek horned-rim glasses resting on perfect cheekbones? I wiped the product of my effort under the floral cushions. Fuck it, no one else will ever use this couch. I thought I was right.

Needless to say, I was not trapped in Des Moines like my friends had figured. They expected me to hate him. "He's an anchor! You need to sail free, man," they would say. I didn't resent him. I did deflower his couch, but that was more a matter of convenience. In fact, I liked the feeling of life on hold. I did exactly what was expected of me, and that was enough. The days had gone so fast in Chicago, but then again, I drank too much coffee and smoked too much dope, so I can't reasonably expect my mind to hold a steady grip on those memories. In Des Moines, things didn't happen unless they had to. The days limped by. Now that I finally had time to myself, I didn't know what to do with it, and I liked it.

My routine was interrupted one morning when the car wouldn't start. It was no surprise, really. The sickly Taurus had it coming. We sat for several minutes looking out at the haggard bricks drunkenly lining the perimeter of the driveway, no doubt leftover from the building's construction. I could tell they weren't put there intentionally—time had put them there.

"What's wrong?" he asked as I tried twisting the key again—it was my only plan of action.

"It won't start; it's broken." I opened the door and popped the hood. Hiding behind it, I flipped open my iPhone and found the number for a local mechanic. I pretended to make adjustments to the engine for a few minutes after the call, carefully distributing grease evenly on my hands and arms. "Well, it's worse than I thought.

I had to call in a mechanic." I made a point of showing off my greasy hands. Why? He would forget all about it in twenty minutes. He would forget about anything in twenty minutes. I got back into the car.

"Grandpa?"

"Yes?"

"I'm gay."

"I know."

I didn't have a chance to respond. Mr. McGregor knocked on the window, nursing a fresh Tom Collins. I hesitantly rolled it down.

"Don't you shitheads know anything 'bout cars?"

"Don't curse, you old asshole!" yelled Ms. Macy from her chair.

"Why don't you come over here an' say that to my face?"

"I have too much self-respect to talk to you."

"Shut up an' play yer game!"

"Solitaire is not a game; it is a state of mind." Ms. Macy kept her gaze on the cards, mechanically flipping them in threes onto the plank of pine on her lap. Mr. McGregor turned to me.

"Women—can't live with 'em, can't live without 'em! I bet young bloods like you get all the tail you want these days! Not in my time, no sir! In the army, it's men, men, men, all the time. Anyways, ain't no way a women ever touched an engine! Lemme take a look . . . ," Mr. McGregor flexed with the confidence of Rosie the Riveter as he limped behind the hood. He returned a few minutes later without his Tom Collins, his hands and arms covered with grease. "It's worse 'en I thought . . . You're gonna need to call a mechanic."

On cue, a truck pulled into the driveway. The mechanic strutted towards the car, flashing a smile as she went behind the hood. Mr. McGregor's eyes went wide.

He tried to say something, but only managed to induce a coughing fit. Ms. Macy began to laugh. I can't remember the mechanic's face, but Mr. McGregor's cherry tomato grimace is as clear as day. A new fuel filter did the trick, and it didn't take the mechanic long to install. I paid her whatever she wanted without question—I didn't know cars had fuel filters. Mr. McGregor retrieved his Tom Collins and returned, defeated, to his chair. I got back in the car.

"I know what we will do today," my grandfather said, buckling his seat belt. I stared at him, wondering what he knew. He fidgeted towards the left pocket of his khaki slacks, and pulled out a handkerchief. "It will take us the rest of the afternoon, but I don't have much to do here anyways," he said, wiping his glasses with the product of his pocket.

"Me neither."

We had driven all the way past Ames on Highway 35, and still I didn't know where we were going. My mind was racing alongside the car, his words haunting my skull. I had only opened the closet door once when I was nearly blackout drunk, confiding in friends too tranquilized to care. Now I had thrown my secret through the filter of an old man's memory, expecting it to pass through the patchwork undetected. He had known all along, or at least pretended to know, and now it was his move.

Out of the corner of my eye, I observed him quietly watching the Iowa afternoon. He seemed captivated by the conglomerate green mass of corn stalks scraping the skyline, no doubt a sight he had seen all his life. I know now that eventually the mundane matures into nostalgia, melancholy replaces ambition, and what's leftover is called wisdom. Having moved past trying to change the world years ago, he was content to watch it run its course. He was just along for the ride, but then again, so was I—and in that moment, we almost understood each other.

Not a word was spoken until an hour later when we turned up around the west side of Clear Lake, our stomachs aching for attention. "Let's make a pit stop," he said. "One tank is empty; the other tank is full."

The diner looked like an emasculated boxcar with its wheels cut off. A flaky white sign hovered above a bloated screen door, but it was too chipped to read. I sat down at a table while he went to the bathroom and looked at the ruins around me. The interior had inadvertently stayed true to the fifties, and time had done its part to reveal the skeleton of old trends. Tarnished chrome counter tops dimly reflected sunlight over faded checkered tiles—the decor of tomorrow. Funny then, that by idolizing a future furnished in shiny metals, the diner had been cursed to endure the forlorn existence of an unintentional gimmick.

Grandpa returned from the bathroom, and we ordered coffee from a baggy-eyed waitress smoking a cigarette (city laws don't apply). She went into the kitchen, and we were alone.

"Why are we here?"

"Well, isn't that the $64,000 question." He smiled, folding his hands.

"Have you been here before?"

"Maybe, it would've been a long time ago. When I was your age, I spent some summer weekends fishing for bass on Clear Lake with Guy Lawrence and Billy Shim. We would hitchhike from Des Moines with a cooler full of beer and whiskey. If I ever came here, it would've been with them."

The tired waitress reappeared with a steaming mug in each hand. Her self-contempt seeped into the coffee—a sad and bitter brew awaited us. "This place is a dump," he said, reaching for his mug. I nodded my head and did the same.

We ate lunch quickly and got back in the car. I started heading south towards Highway 35, a straight shot to Des Moines. It was late in the afternoon, and Grandpa was due for a nap. "Make sure he takes two naps a day!" my mother said once.

"Two naps a day? He might as well be in a coma," I told her, but she never liked my jokes . . . no one did. (She always secretly liked my sisters better—they didn't have to tell jokes to get attention!) I flipped the turn signal, and Grandpa let out a grunt of frustration.

"What are you doing? We didn't drive all the way out here to turn around!"

"What?" I pulled over. "How can I know which way to go if you don't give me directions?"

"Turn around, then take a right on 8th Street for

about five miles, then we'll take a right onto a gravel road. From there we'll go about a mile down, and that's it." I was taken aback. "Some things stick with you," he said.

I followed his route out past the paved road, into the middle of nowhere.

We parked on the edge of the gravel, and I instinctively locked the car. The field before us was free of corn. Heaps of dried grass took advantage of the available real estate. Grandpa led the way, walking cautiously through the tall grass. I followed hesitantly, watching him carefully. I worried that he had finally gone off the deep end, and yet, he seemed so sure of himself—I was just along for the ride. Then, there they were—sleek black-horned rim glasses, poking out of the grass fifty yards ahead.

They were built for a giant, hanging on two thick pale stakes for support.

"Here we are—Buddy Holly's crash site," he said, sighing at the glasses.

"Crash site?"

"The plane carrying Buddy Holly, Ritchie Valens, and the Big Bopper crashed here on February 3, 1959—the day the music died."

"How did you remember that?"

"I don't know. You can't choose what you remember." He walked forward and put his hand on the glasses.

"Guy Lawrence, Billy Shim, and me would sneak out here and camp under the stars. We would drink and stay up late, hoping to see Buddy's ghost. You see, Buddy means a lot to me, and I know he means a lot to you too."

"What do you mean?"

"Well, he's the guy you're always moaning about, right?"

"Moaning?"

"Yes, you're always going off in your sleep about Buddy Holly and his glasses. It wakes me up sometimes." I froze—my face went pale. I had greatly underestimated his hearing aid.

"I'm sorry about that."

"Don't be. Buddy would be on the top of my list!" His face lit up in a smile.

"I can't believe you heard me wanking off to those Buddy Holly records! I'm embarrassed."

"You wanked off to my Buddy Holly records? What the hell, Simon!"

"I thought you knew . . ."

"Those are original pressings!"

He snipped at me all the way back to Des Moines, lecturing on both the financial and sentimental value of his records. I told him that I liked driving in silence, but he didn't shut up until we saw the ambulance outside the apartment.

Ms. Macy's family came a week later, loaded her things into a truck, and left within thirty minutes of arriving. Ironic, then, that the object that saw most of her attention still lay against the front stoop, free of cards forever. Mr. McGregor died alone four weeks later when he had a heart attack while playing solitaire. A couple from out east moved in, and the cycle continued. It's scary how fast a person can vanish, scarier still that Grandpa didn't remember them by the end of the summer.

Over the next few months, he started to forget more things—the year, the names of my mom and sisters, and how to use the bathroom by himself. He saw the world as a stranger, and he would never get back in touch. He was lost in himself, his mind now filled with unfamiliar pathways leading to dead end after dead end.

I wondered if I would be the same someday. We gave his furniture to Goodwill after he checked into the hospital. His vitals were bad, so the nurses let me bring in a record player. I put the needle in the groove, and as Buddy Holly & The Crickets jumped into a familiar song, I imagined hitchhiking up to Clear Lake with Guy Lawrence and Billy Shim. I imagined drinking beer and whiskey while fishing for dinner. I even imagined watching the sunset in the grassy patch beneath the giant horned-rim glasses, silently waiting for Buddy Holly's ghost.

To: My grandpa

BarryBonds!

But THANK GOD you
didn't look this ugly!!!

Happy Birthday!
From: Henry

Bopa, you
may be
getting old. . .

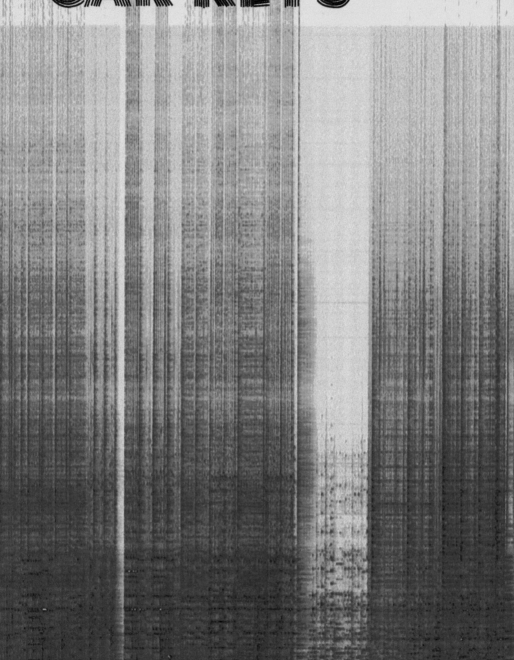

CAR KEYS

I lost the car keys.
I have been searching the house for hours and found nothing. I need those keys. I need those keys more than anything else, and I can't find them.

I have tried retracing my steps, but my memory fades, and I can't even remember what I had for breakfast. "Did I have breakfast?" I say aloud. I look in the sink and find no evidence of breakfast or the car keys. The sink is useless to me. Everything is useless but the car keys. I need them.

I stumble through the rooms of my house overturning every object, and opening all the cabinets and drawers. I find nothing other than a few letters I wrote but never sent to my love interests over the years. I throw them away.

I quickly walk away from the garbage bin, but then sprint back to it, digging through the waste of my life in search of what I desperately need. I find hopelessness at the bottom of the bin, and return to my search.

I feel sweat drip down my face, and I smell worse than the garbage bin. I pass a mirror and catch a glimpse of a monster. I normally look somewhat approachable, but now my hair droops over my tired eyes, and a vein bulges from my forehead. I continue.

My search tactics have become more aggressive over the hours, and I rip through any obstacle that could possibly hide the keys. As I tear apart my bed, I begin sobbing. The tears flow freely down my face, and I mumble to myself.

"Help!" I say. "Help me!" I begin shouting. "Help me, Lord! Help me find what I search for!" I have been an atheist up to this point, but the only thing left to try is divine intervention.

I fall to the floor. The tears have stopped. I think. If they find that car, they will put me away forever. I am out of options now. I have used up all my hope and will. I look over at the garbage bin and think. I think of all I've wasted, all the opportunities I've thrown away. I close my eyes and reach under the bed. With one shot, I waste everything.

"Poor kid. These things are such a shame," says one officer to the other. "You hate to see things like this," the other officer responds. He scribbles on his notepad.

"Does he have any identification?" asks the first officer. The second officer kneels down to the body and searches it.

"Anything?" asks the first officer.

"Nothing but the car keys in his pocket," the second officer replies.

PLAYING WITH FIRE

You cut down a green leaf tree
and built a home in your head.playing with fire
Everything outside your hazy world
just don't seem to make sense.
While you played with fire
your youth expired,
with a spark lighting up a dream,
if you keep swimming in
a cynical lake
you'll drown out reality.
So who,
is gonna fire the gun
at your starting line,
and who,
is gonna pick up the tab
when you don't give a dime,
and who,
is gonna chase the sun
and go far.
Oh brother
it shouldn't have to be this hard.

POKÉMON CARD

Ian Shank

When I was in first grade, I remember always looking forward to dinner at the Mackaman's house. Part of it, I think, was just because of how their house looked— with its winding hardwood staircases, it always seemed supernaturally large and mysterious compared to our yellow stucco bungalow—and part of it was because it meant I got to see Henry.

At the time, I was fairly certain Henry was the most hilarious big kid the Twin Cities had ever seen. He was several years older than me—the brother of my younger brother's friend, Owen—and was probably just playing the frighteningly good nine-year-old host every time his parents informed him that we were on our way. That is, at least, kind of what I want to believe, since hanging out with six-year-old me was often a huge drag.

One night in particular I remember chilling in Henry's room upstairs, shooting the shit in the classic way of late-nineties children: discussing Pokémon. By this point I had amassed an absolutely extraordinary (read: nauseating) range of the cardboard playing cards, but Henry wanted to show me something truly special.

"It's a holographic Dragonite," he proudly explained, eliciting the kind of raw envy only a very immature child could feel for a derpy picture of cartoon dragon.

"Wow . . . " I quietly exhaled.

Deftly, tenderly, he twirled the card in his hand a few times, making the light play of the glimmering backdrop, before suddenly turning and holding it out to me.

"Here," he said, "you can look at it if you want."

Palms outstretched, I cradled the card in my hand as if

it were some kind of fragile, ancient talisman. I traced its cardboard contours—coveting its every square centimeter—practically salivating at its sheer brilliance. And then, right then and there, I resolved to steal it.

In practice, the theft proved extremely easy. Of course it helped that, unlike Henry, I had few scruples, and even fewer qualms with my precocious narcissism. But in the end, I think I just pocketed the card when Henry stepped out of the room.

The guilt set in almost immediately after leaving the house. I'd pull the shimmering card out of my pocket on the school bus and the shame and regret would well up right with it, spreading through my body like an icy flood of remorse. Maybe it was from being handled so continuously, but Dragonite's once-majestic visage seemed increasingly drab and lifeless by the day. "I have betrayed him," I chastised myself. "I am a monster."

The next time we returned to the Mackaman's the card came with me. By now it was severely wrinkled, having lost much of its former luster clutched between my clammy fingers. But still, I knew I had to repent.

When I eventually found Henry in his room, I meekly pulled the card from my pocket and tried to explain what I had done. I stuttered and muttered my way to an apology, averting my eyes until the moment I handed the card back to him.

Looking up, I remember surprise flashing across his face. Maybe he hadn't even noticed the card was gone in the first place, or maybe he thought it had been misplaced, and had already accepted it as lost. Either way, the expression was fleeting.

Without a hint of anger, he smiled his goofy grin and thanked me—actually thanked me—for giving it back. And the crazy thing is, I think he actually meant it.

Henry, Meredith, and Owen.
By James (Dooby) Richards.

WALTER FRAZIER IS DEAD

My name is Walter Frazier,

and I have been dead for ten years. The doctors said all those years of smoking finally caught up to me, but I don't regret a thing. One thing I do regret was requesting a proper Christian burial. This is not to say that I don't believe in God or Christianity in general, but seeing as I am in neither heaven nor hell, I have my doubts. As it turns out, you don't travel to St. Peter's gate upon the release of your last breath, and I'm afraid to say the truth is not nearly so whimsical. When my heart stopped beating, I simply, was. I can't move my limbs, or blink my eyes. I can't hear, feel, or see, all my bodily senses gone, numb, trapped. I sure do a lot of thinking, but I suppose thinking is all I can do.

Anyways, as time went by, I concluded that being dead is pretty lonely, which is why I decided that I should've been cremated. That way, I wouldn't be all alone, trapped in this damn body in this damn grave. My body may be my own personal vessel, but still after all this time I can't find the damn eject button. Damn. Well, I suppose if life is just the passing of time, death isn't much different. Life was a whole lot more fun though; there are cigarettes in life.

I like to relive my life, start to end, to pass the time. I'm afraid I forgot a good bit of it, which is why it only takes me a week to get through my entire life. If that seems pathetic, why don't you try the same? Notice how there are a few key moments that stick out to you; the first time you saw your baby brother, the last time you saw your baby brother, or what about the silent snowy evening when you kissed the only girl you ever loved for the first and last time?

||

Owen and Henry Mackaman.

SILENT SPECTERS

Aching eyes upon the skyline
Disenchanting visions haunt their minds
Specters come forth
Silent in their gaze
Laminating stagnant cisterns
Caging the morning dew
Stretching draught cascades 'cross
The grilled grass
Empty branches quiver
Hovering o'er dusty plains
Like empty extended callous hands
Shrill screams cast shadows
O'er the sands
Cracking the clay!
The mortar turns loose
The ancient chapels crumble
As the specters stand resolute

FAN DEATH

Nobody is immune
Everyone will try
Nobody is immune
Everyone will die

Table of Contents/Tracklist

Carroll - Out Here

GREY(coyote) - One Day Been

Strange Names - Luxury Child

Gloss - Ian's Dream

Hollow Boys - Hater

Strange Relations - Ghost World

Nice Purse - Broken Filthy Arrows

Teenage Moods - Golden Lasso

Nallo - All Summer

Miami Dolphins - Doodler

Human Kindness - Ahoy! St. Croix!

Prissy Clerks - Losing Time

The Velveteens- mama

Bad Bad Hats - It Hurts

Free Download at:
http://www.mediafire.com/?lf9t7t30qvfrj6u

This mix is dedicated to the memory of Henry Mackaman,
guitarist of Phantom Vibration. His talent and warmness
has had a huge impact the Twin Cities music scene, as
well as all who met him. He will be greatly missed.

Macalester radio station,
WMCN 91.7 FM, mixed tape.

Dedicated to Henry
April 2013

FINALLY, HENRY HAS SHOWN ME MY REASON TO LIVE.

LOOKING THROUGH ALL OF THE KIND WORDS PEOPLE HAVE POSTED ABOUT HIM, IT IS ABUNDANTLY CLEAR THAT HENRY MADE A DEEP IMPACT ON EVERYONE HE MET.

HIS OLDEST FRIENDS, PEOPLE HE HAD ONLY EVER MET ONCE, AND PEOPLE WHO HE'D ONLY RECENTLY MET, ALL RECOUNTED THEIR TALES OF HENRY'S AMIABILITY, HIS INCREDIBLE TALENT AND KNOWLEDGE, AND ALL OF THE GREAT MEMORIES HE HAD GIVEN THEM.

SO MANY LIVES, IMPACTED SO INTENSELY BY ONE PERSON. THESE MEMORIES ARE HENRY'S LEGACY.

TO IMPROVE THE LIVES OF EVERY PERSON HE EVER INTERACTED WITH, EVEN IF ALL THAT MEANT WAS GRINNING WIDE AND LETTING LOOSE HIS GOOFY LAUGH, IS HOW HENRY SPENT HIS YEARS IN THIS LIFE.

I KNOW THAT THIS IS HOW I AM MEANT TO SPEND MY LIFE. AND FOR TEACHING ME THIS ONE, FINAL LESSON, I LOVE YOU, HENRY MACKAMAN.

Brogan James
From "My reason to live"
April 12, 2013

AN UNTIMELY DEATH

Dressed in a black robe,
a woman cries at the funeral.

I tell her that I'm not really dead,
I tell everyone I'm not really dead,
but
the priest slaps my face every time I speak;
my cheek hurts,
so I stay silent.
At least the food is good—
the deli down the street catered,
and
as far as last meals go,
it's not bad,
but
the funeral isn't perfect by any means—
I've never met anyone here, and

the picture by the casket
looks nothing like me.

Henry Mackaman
1991 - 2013

Henry Mackaman left an indelible mark on WSUM in his time as a DJ through his show <u>The Grooving Tree</u>, his band "Phantom Vibration," and through his relationship with his many friends here.

We loved not only the tunes he spun, but also the joy and passion he displayed for music and for life.

He is missed but never forgotten.

Commissioned by Dave Black,
WSUM General Manager.

DEAR MEREDITH,

BARE TREES, FREEZING LAKES, AND SNOW COVERING ALL USHERS IN THE SEASON OF REFLECTION ON THE PAST YEARS' EVENTS; THE ANGUISH, DARKNESS, FRUSTRATION, AND GRIEF. YET, THERE IS MUCH TO BE THANKFUL FOR—ESPECIALLY HENRY AND HIS GENEROUS GIFT OF LIFE.

HAVING WRITTEN ONLY LECTURES AND SCIENTIFIC PAPERS, THERE IS AN IMMENSE FEELING

OF INELOQUENCE IN ATTEMPTING TO PUT INTO WORDS HOW I FEEL ABOUT EVENTS OF THE LAST YEAR. REST ASSURED THAT THERE IS NOT A WAKING HOUR THAT GOES BY THAT I DON'T THINK ABOUT HENRY, AND IT HAS BECOME A MORNING RITUAL TO SAY "THANKS, HENRY."

THE SPIRIT OF HENRY STILL LIVES IN US ALL.

Excerpts from a letter
from Walt Goodman
Professor at the
University of Wisconsin, Madison
Henry's heart recipient

UW HEALTH TRANSPLANT PROGRAM
Where hope and gratitude meet, courage thrives

50 Years of Courage

UW Health
University of Wisconsin
Transplant Program

Meredith holds a photo of her son, Henry, whose heart beats in Walter.

BECOME AN ORGAN DONOR AT WWW.DMV. ORG/ORGAN-DONOR.PHP

HENRY

by Milton Snoeyenbos

We never knew you, Henry, but we knew
That still you have joined our conversation.
Although this may not seem to make much sense,
In your absence you are still a presence.
Our conversation rises out of love,
Which is the overseer of all things.
As Keats well knew of young men who have passed,
Love is one thing that never fades but lasts.

We never knew your music, yet we hear
It universally reverberate.
For music, as a messenger of love,
Embraces every place in all of space.
And, unlike language, music spans all time.
Music is the universal language,
Obliterating death and mortal pain,
Enabling us to realize your love.

TRUE TO FORM AND TENDER-NESS

Each tick stings
with each step
A familiar face does disappear
The setting sun faded with days between
our distance grows as stretching vines,
But I did love you then
in that foreign time,
and I love you now.

LIFE IS SO FRAGILE, BUT YOU ARE SO STRONG, AND ALTHOUGH IT WOULD BE EASY TO CRUMBLE IN THE FACE OF TRAGEDY, I KNOW YOU WILL DO NO SUCH THING.

OF COURSE, YOU WILL UNDOUBTEDLY LEAVE GALWAY A CHANGED PERSON, AND ALTHOUGH IT'S HARD TO SAY WHAT WILL CHANGE EXACTLY, YOU WILL MOST CERTAINLY BE A BONA FIDE ADULT. SCARY, RIGHT?
(I KNOW . . .)

WHAT I'M GETTING AT IS SOMETHING YOU ALREADY KNOW;
MAKE THE MOST OF IT, DO WHAT YOU WANT TO DO,

AND LIVE A LIFE OF LOVE
AND ADVENTURE.
I AM SO LUCKY TO HAVE
YOU AS MY FRIEND, AND
SO THANKFUL FOR ALL THE
TIME WE'VE HAD.

SO WHEN YOU'RE AT THE
PUB AFTER CLASS,
WHEN THE TIME COMES, BE
SURE TO RAISE A GLASS,
TO ALL FUTURE DAYS AND
ALL DAYS PAST,
TO FRIEND AND FOE, ALL
THE PEOPLE YOU KNOW,
AND DRINK TO GOOD TIMES
AND THAT LONG THEY WILL
LAST.

-H

Excerpt from a letter Henry
sent to Madelyne Heyman
after Tamar Kaplan died.
January 2013

Normandy 2012
Watercolor by Susan Crawford Stevens.

COURAGE TO CONTINUE—

THAT COUNTS.

-from Henry's journal.

I'm afraid it's the end of the show. But thanks for tuning in. It's been fun.

You've been listening to WSUM, and I'm going to call the show quits with a song from...

THE
GROOVING TREE

NEW BEGINNINGS

Joseph Chybowski was Henry's night nurse at Meriter Hospital. As Henry lay dying, Joseph treated Henry with loving kindness. He talked to him as if he were still able to hear. There was so much grace in his tenderness.

These were the darkest days of my life. Yet Joseph brought a familial sense of calm and caring. He let me crawl into Henry's tiny ICU bed at night and read his Caring Bridge messages to him from the hospital's computer. He was my caregiver as well. He rubbed my back as I cried and smiled as I showed him photos of Henry.

The last morning of Henry's life, Joseph stayed with us. He gently touched his head and called him a hero. I will never forget that moment.

Joseph and his wife, Amy, are now a part of my extended family. And their family continues to grow. They have a little girl named Lucy and just recently added a little boy. They named him Henry Lewis.

Even though a chapter of my life ended, new beginnings emerge.

Henry's love grows.

Meredith Leigh

Joseph and Henry Chybowski

A NOTE ON THE BOOK DESIGN

The toughest part of designing this book was choosing what *not* to be inspired by. We had a whole oceanic trench of Henry artifacts to sift through, edit, and organize into a cohesive book. Many themes surfaced in the process (waves, echoes, music, death, vibrations, and memories, to name a few stand-outs). I tried to enhance these themes with few design elements:

Typefaces and line art—Margs, Henry's girlfriend, set the visual tone of the book. Margs illustrated the cover and created the H2 typeface (used for author names) from Henry's handwriting. I chose the H1 typeface (used for titles) for its likeness to the spinning record in the awesome "corner gif" that she created for the book.

Gradients—A wide gradient of bright yellow to deep navy set the color palette for the book. Our hope was to strike a balance between the bright light Henry was as a person, and the deep, dark topics his creative work often grappled with. A gradient is a segment of the color spectrum, and spectra of all kinds were themes in Henry's life and writing.

Sound maps—Sound is also a spectrum. Henry's lifelong fascination with music inspired me to incorporate sound-mapping into the design. The title pages feature spectrograms (sound maps) of song from his band, Phantom Vibration, and the quote pages feature chromagrams (sound graphs) made from recordings of his radio show.

Shannon Fletcher

ACKNOWL-EDGMENTS

The words to explain the devastation of the sudden death of our grandson Henry simply do not exist. Our journey to compile a suitable tribute to his life and creativity began about two years ago when we met Hanna Kjeldbjerg, a young editor at Beaver's Pond Press. Hanna, who was close to Henry's age, received a large collection of material that we had saved over the years, along with material from Henry's mom, Meredith.

Hanna, who never met Henry, has woven his story into a beautiful and insightful narration of his life and work. We cannot thank Hanna enough for what she has so lovingly accomplished.

And now she knows Henry too.

David and Cordy Strand

TO SPEND
MORE TIME
WITH HENRY,
OR GROOVE
WITH HIM TO
HIS DJ SETS
OR PHANTOM
VIBRATION
ALBUMS,
VISIT

HENRYMACKAMAN.COM

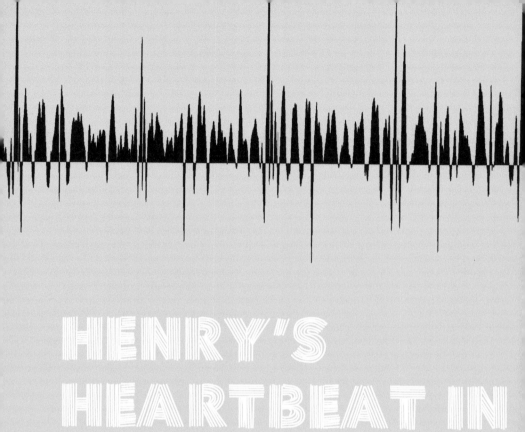

HENRY'S HEARTBEAT IN WAVEFORM.

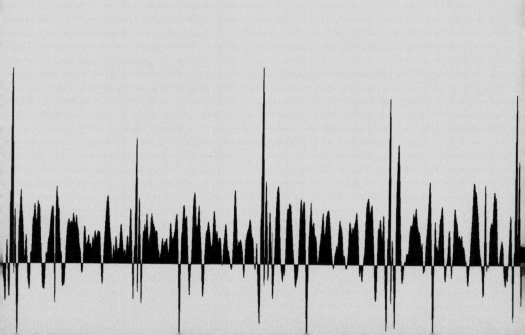

Walter Goodman, Henry's heart recipient.

HENRY LIVES
ON & ON